The KINDERGARTEN BOOK

ENLARGED EDITION

By LILLA BELLE PITTS
Professor Emeritus of Music Education
Teachers College, Columbia University, New York

MABELLE GLENN
Formerly Director of Music
Public Schools, Kansas City, Missouri

LORRAIN E. WATTERS
Director of Music
Public Schools, Des Moines, Iowa

and LOUIS G. WERSEN
Director of Music Education
Public Schools, Philadelphia, Pennsylvania

ILLUSTRATIONS BY Joan Esley, Margo Pisillo
and Ruth Wood

GINN AND COMPANY

BOSTON · NEW YORK · CHICAGO · ATLANTA · DALLAS · PALO ALTO · TORONTO · LONDON

Acknowledgments

Acknowledgment is due to publishers, composers, and authors for permission to reprint songs and poems in this book, as follows:

DOROTHY BARUCH, "Barber's Clippers," from *I Like Machinery*; the Estate of KATHARINE LEE BATES, "America the Beautiful"; BASIL BLACKWELL and Mrs. SYLVIA CHESTERMAN, "The Coal Man," by HUGH CHESTERMAN; "There Was a Boy," from *Father Goose: His Book*, by L. FRANK BAUM; BEHRMAN HOUSE, Inc., "Doll's Lullaby," from *Gateway to Jewish Song*, by EISENSTEIN; JONATHAN CAPE, Limited, London, a stanza of "Nature's Friend," from *Collected Poems*, by W. H. DAVIES; CHILD LIFE, excerpts from "The Road to Raffydiddle," by MILDRED MEIGS, "Farm Life," by RUTH EDNA STANTON, and "A Little Seed," by WILHELMINA SEEGMILLER; *The Churchman*, "A Pumpkin Speaks," by AMANDA BARRIS; Mrs. KATHERINE DENT, "When You Send a Valentine" (words only), by MILDRED J. HILL, from EMILIE POULSSON's *Holiday Songs*; DODD, MEAD & COMPANY, Inc., stanzas from "The World's Music," by GABRIEL SETOUN; DOUBLEDAY & COMPANY, Inc., "Mother," from *Fairies and Chimneys*, by ROSE FYLEMAN, copyrighted 1920, and "The Animal Store," from *Taxis and Toadstools*, by RACHEL FIELD, copyrighted 1926; THE EXPRESSION COMPANY, "Skipping Is Fun," by PAUL EDMONDS, "Puppy's Tail" and "Tippy Tiptoe," all from *Speech Improvement through Choral Speaking*; EDWINA FALLIS, "Wise Johnny"; GINN AND COMPANY and the editors of THE WORLD OF MUSIC, "We're Wooden Soldiers Marching," from *Sing a Song*, copyrighted 1936, and "Little Ducky Duddle," from *Listen and Sing*, copyrighted 1936, 1943; GRACE GLAUBITZ, "Walking"; HARPER & BROTHERS, "Please, Everybody, Look at Me" and "My Zipper Suit," from *A Pocketful of Rhymes*, by MARY LOUISE ALLEN, copyright 1939, and "Trains," from *I Go A-Traveling*, by JAMES S. TIPPETT, copyright 1929, and "Cricket," from *I Know Some Little Animals*, by JAMES S. TIPPETT, copyright 1941; HOUGHTON MIFFLIN COMPANY, "When People Say," from *All about Me*, by JOHN DRINKWATER; LAIDLAW BROTHERS, Inc., "The Clock" and "Teddy Bear," from *Song Primer*, by ALYS E. BENTLEY;

LONGMANS, GREEN & Co., Inc., "When Cats Get Up in the Morning," "Kitty-Pretty," and "A Song about Me," from *Singing Circle*, by LADY BELL; THE MACMILLAN COMPANY, "Here Is the Beehive" and "My Love for You," from *The Rooster Crows*, by the PETERSHAMS, copyright 1945, and "Lullaby, O Lullaby," from *Poetical Works*, by CHRISTINA ROSSETTI; CLIFFORD H. MEIGS, Executor, an excerpt from "The Road to Raffydiddle," by MILDRED MEIGS; DOROTHY ALDIS, "Everybody Says" and "Hiding," from *Everything and Anything*, copyright 1925, 1926, 1927 by DOROTHY ALDIS and used by courtesy of MINTON, BALCH & COMPANY; G. P. PUTNAM'S SONS, a line from "About Our Play" in *Verses and Fly Leaves*, by CHARLES STUART CALVERLEY; RAND McNALLY & COMPANY, "An Evening Prayer" and "Night," by ELIZABETH McE. SHIELDS, from *Prayers for Little Children*, edited by Mary Alice Jones, copyright 1937; CHARLES SCRIBNER'S SONS, "Happy Thought" and a stanza of "The Land of Counterpane," from *A Child's Garden of Verses*, by ROBERT LOUIS STEVENSON, and lines from "The Land of Wonder-Wander," from *Poems of Childhood*, by EUGENE FIELD; The Society of Authors, MISS ROSE FYLEMAN, and MESSRS. METHUEN for "Mother," from *Fairies and Chimneys*, by ROSE FYLEMAN; CLAYTON F. SUMMY COMPANY, copyright owners, "Pinky Winky Baby," from *Happy Songs for Little Children*, by IDA C. KNAPP; DOROTHY BROWN THOMPSON, lines from "Plans"; FREDERICK WARNE & Co., Inc., "Ring-a-Ring," from *Marigold Garden*, by KATE GREENAWAY; WHITMAN PUBLISHING COMPANY, "See-Saw," "Going to London," and "Pitter and Patter"; *The Youths' Companion*, "Easter Duck and Easter Chick," by ELSIE PARRISH.

For some of the piano accompaniments in this book the editors wish to express their appreciation to Alice Gallup, Mary Nancy Graham, and Jessie Carter.

In the case of some poems for which acknowledgment is not given, we have earnestly endeavored to find the original source and to procure permission for their use, but without success.

ii

Contents

TEACHING SUGGESTIONS

ABOUT FOLKS · (Page 1)

[Titles in italics indicate instrumental selections]

ABOUT THE WONDERFUL OUTSIDE WORLD · (Page 93)

ABOUT THINGS THAT SING · (Page 123)

❧

SHINING HOURS · (Page 157)

❧

ALPHABETICAL INDEX · (Page 179)

❧

INDEX OF FIRST LINES OF POEMS · (Page 180)

TEACHING SUGGESTIONS

I · *Vocal Expression*

A. Singing

Singing is the basic activity in any well-rounded program of music education. It is also an expressive art that cannot be neglected justifiably in any general curriculum aiming for the fullest personal and social development of all children.

Music is a major means of communication which is capable of being used in ways that will give children better command of all their expressive actions.

To this end singing is especially helpful, for it is a mode of expression that lies close to the personal interests and experiences of children (p. 8, Singing While We Play).

There is warmth, energy, and potential power for creative growth in the untutored singing of children, for children delight in song. Their own feelings—their intuitive natures—tell them that songs are for singing; that songs are to grow on; that "all inmost things . . . are melodious, . . . that all deep things are song" (Carlyle).

Music and childhood go together. It is no wonder that children are full of song, for songs are made of materials that are as common as daily food and drink: sound and movement, play and work, thoughts and words, moods and melodies.

The songs in this book are dedicated to warming the hearts, opening the ears, and freeing the voices of young children, in order that they may better express the innate feeling of kinship that they have for the *singing world* in which they live.

B. The Child Voice

The child voice, as it is heard in the singing of healthy, happy, and hearty children, covers a wide range of variable qualities.

It cannot be said of all children, nor of one child at all times, that the natural child voice is high and light, or thin and delicate, soft and sweet, or of any other uniform or predetermined quality. Too much depends upon when and where a child uses his voice and what the purposes of his singing happen to be.

Children often are found to have *one* voice which they reserve for the formal music lesson, and *many* other voices to use at will in their own self-initiated expressive activities.

If this is assumed to be the case, it is not possible to aim for any one accepted ideal of the "true child voice" which all children must measure up to, regardless of human variability.

Little children must be guided along lines of musical growth that emerge from their normal and everyday curiosities and interests. The techniques of singing and playing have no place in the kindergarten and primary grades.

To provide day-by-day experience in singing songs that have significance to a child is the surest way to make him increasingly sensitive to the differences in the quality of tone which he himself is capable of producing. Finding appropriate ways to express song meanings that hold reality and interest for a child will induce him to listen not only to his own voice but to the singing of others.

Children's desires to understand, to gain a deeper sense of personal satisfaction, and to convey greater pleasure to others are good reasons for them to try to improve enunciation, tone production, and interpretation in singing. These are things that make sense to children and therefore enlist their co-operation.

To reiterate: good tone and beautiful singing in childhood are not brought about by means of specific training in vocal techniques.

Music says something that is very intimate and personal to children. Good singing depends upon the vitality and depth of their response to the message that a song has for them.

Pleasing tone quality, good enunciation, imaginative interpretation, and other values which are important for musical growth should be the anticipated and *expected* outcomes of *expressive singing*, instead of the other way around.

C. Individual Differences in Children's Singing

At every step in the progress of the musical development of children individual differences assert themselves. Nowhere are they more apparent than in the singing voices of children who are entering school for the first time. Besides, the scale of deviation is extremely wide, running the gamut all the way from children who "sing like angels" to those who seem unable to sing at all.

This should not cause undue concern. Individual differences in singing talents and abilities are to be expected in any heterogeneous group of young children. Nevertheless, in planning a program of music education that will give every child a chance to improve himself, it is necessary to know how to diagnose, classify, and guide children who are retarded in their singing responses.

1. In the *first* group there are children who are uncertain and confused in their singing, owing to inexpe-

rience. The children found in this group have had either a meager or a haphazard musical background in the home.

In a rich and stimulating environment these children will have little difficulty in "finding their singing voices." What they need most are the favorable circumstances provided by a broad program of vivid and varied singing experiences.

2. In a *second* group are children who are too immature to adapt themselves to a singing standard set by the majority of their classmates. Children who are "young for their years" rarely get either the tunes or the words of songs as readily as is normal. Compared with the rest of their group, they tend to fall behind in both physical co-ordination and social co-operation. It does no good to try to push an immature child. Each boy and girl should be guided and encouraged to take part in a widening range of musical activities, but at the same time should be allowed to make adjustments, each at his own rate of speed.

An adequate music program has to make special provision for meeting all kinds of individual differences. Short and simple songs that can be grasped with ease and many well-known singing games should be included. These little folks need a chance to join in, on their level, with what the others can do. Independence is built up step by step through active, happy, and successful participation.

3. In a *third* classification there are children who may be designated as indifferent singers. Numerous reasons can be found for inertia and a seeming lack of interest in singing. At one extreme there are children who have been overentertained and overfed. At the other end of the scale there are children who may have been dulled by underprivilege and malnutrition.

Singing problems arising from these two extremes, with gradations in between, are present in many classrooms. They are seldom easy to solve, but are far from hopeless. Overcoming them, however, depends on the same two factors that are critically important in all learning situations. One is the right environment; the other, the right teacher. Assuming the existence of the first, how then to arouse and nurture musical growth in boys and girls who are apathetic from too little and what to do with children who are fagged or pampered by overabundance call for as much tact and resourcefulness as a teacher can muster.

4. The *fourth* variance may take in only a very small proportion (maybe none) of a given group of children, but it should be mentioned; for specialists are found oftener than is either commonly supposed or observed in early childhood. Nearly always they are precocious boys or girls who have developed some one consuming interest, one that is so all-absorbing that it shuts out music in any of its manifestations,—that is, unless music happens to be the engrossing interest. Even so, a problem is present,

for children of this kind are individualistic in both tastes and tendencies, making it hard to deal with them in ordinary school situations. They are usually ahead of their group in their ability to deal with ideas, words, and other media of expression. Consequently the songs and other materials used in musical activities suitable for general use seem babyish to an exceptional child.

The problem in such cases is not one of teaching a child to sing or to respond to music, but that of arousing him to an awareness of broader social and cultural opportunities which may well engage his attention and interest. The teacher who can induce a self-centered and self-sufficient child to assume responsibility for helping those who are immature and inexperienced has started him on the surest road to self-help.

5. In a *fifth* category are children who fail to rise to their highest level of individual singing ability because of emotional disturbances. By far the largest number of boys and girls who are referred to variously as nonsingers, uncertain, retarded, or backward singers; as tone-deaf pupils, monotones, or sufferers from some other tonal anomaly will be found in this division.

All too often children form extremely unfavorable attitudes toward singing, owing to quite understandable emotional disorders. It may be that a child is excessively timid, fearful, or jealous, or it may be that feelings of insecurity, frustration, or inferiority are at the root of his vocal disabilities.

The best cure for emotional disturbances that have an unhappy effect upon the social and expressive activities of children is the proverbial ounce of prevention, and it should begin at home. Instead, many well-meaning parents are unintentionally responsible for starting the trouble.

A thoughtless or joking remark made to or in the presence of a child about his or her singing may make a deep and lasting impression on a sensitive boy or girl. It is a mistake to assume that children always know how to interpret casual statements, such as: "Tom can't carry a tune, he takes after his father's family"; "you should hear Peggy sing, her voice is too funny for words," etc., etc. But overpraise of the more gifted child in a family and finding fault with the one who does not do so well can have even a worse effect. Jealousy and resentment follow many a child to school, causing either a stubbornly negative or an openly hostile attitude toward all singing.

Teachers are not free from blame in this respect either. With the best intentions a teacher can make mistakes in dealing with children who are backward in singing that defeat her own good purposes. Usually this comes from failing to recognize the close relationship that exists between the expressive activities and the emotions of children. Feelings in childhood are keener than in later years, for children are gradually building up ideals of themselves. Consciously and unconsciously they are extremely sensitive to the impressions they make on others.

A child yearns to be liked, to please, and to be accepted and wanted. The young have no other way to build confidence in themselves or in their future. Whoever destroys this may have done irreparable harm, for childhood grievances can be lasting, often creating resentments that are never outlived.

Therefore what every teacher and parent should be aware of and ponder over is that the attitudes of children toward singing are formed by a variety of individual and social experiences that are colored by intensely emotional overtones. The very self of a child goes out in song, evoking feelings similar to the emotion that accompanies a gesture of affection or a friendly smile. When this is rebuffed or discouraged, a quiveringly sensitive spot may be touched, making a child feel much as he would had a personal overture of affection or friendliness been rejected with a frown of disapproval. To reiterate a vitally important point: if there is one urgency that is stronger than another in young children, it is the need to belong, to contribute, and to be wanted. Undue concern about how talented a child is, how well he can match tones, or whether or not his singing is as good as that of some other boy or girl has the tendency to create uncertainty and fear (if the child recognizes it).

A teacher can diagnose her pupils' needs without formal testing of voices. In the imitative songs and games every child shows his personality and voice possibilities. The fact that the teacher knows which children can carry a tune and which cannot is locked up in the teacher's mind and heart, and from this starting point she will give each child an opportunity to develop in his own way.

6. In the *last* group there are the fewest, if any—namely, children with physiological handicaps.

Structural deviations in the vocal mechanism that cause children to speak with difficulty will, as a matter of course, have a similar effect upon singing. A cleft palate, malformations of tongue, dental arches, and other structural irregularities usually result in an inability to sing. So, in some instances, will nervous disorders and poor muscular co-ordination.

Frequently the serious nature of underlying conditions requires the advice of both medical and speech experts. In such cases what is left for the teacher to do is to help a child to build as high a level of musical responsiveness as possible with his remaining abilities.

Rhythmic activities covering free and imitative play and experiments with informal instruments are usually well adapted to the individual needs of children in this category. (See pages xiv–xvii, *Rhythmic Expression*, and page 137, *About Other Things That Sing*.)

Successful experiences with music that a child can manage without strain or tensions may eventually encourage him to attempt the more complex action patterns involved in vocal expression.

It is well to keep in mind that while handicapped singers need stimulation and encouragement in some instances, there are others where casual treatment and relaxing activities are equally important.

When the teacher is experimenting with a child who needs special help, she can and must do it in such a way that the self-confidence of that child is not disturbed.

A child either sings or he doesn't before he enters school, and he never thinks of himself as either a *nonsinger* or an *uncertain* singer. But when something happens that dampens his spirit or makes him self-conscious or discourages him, he may become confused about something that would clear up in the natural course of his adaptation to a wealth of varied, appropriate, and well-balanced musical experiences. At no time, in or out of school, should a child be made to feel that his singing or anything else he does is queer, peculiar, or unpleasant. It may be different; but one child differs from another in many respects. Some need to improve themselves in one way, some in other ways, but all need to work and play together; else the social motivation that is so important to all growth and learning is absent.

Correctness and purity of tone, *in the beginning stages of musical growth*, are not so important as *wanting* to sing and having a chance to sing with all one's heart. Singing, like talking, is learned best in social situations where each child is given an opportunity to *take part* at *his* highest level of ability.

A child doing his bit in game and dialogue songs (pp. 5, 38–43, 113), in dramatizations (pp. 63–70), and in imitative tonal (pp. 114–115) and rhythmic play (pp. 125–126, 131–135) is aroused to a lively interest in music that will enable him to find his singing voice in his *own good time*; for children differ in rates of growth as well as in the quality of their voices.

An approach of this kind recognizes that children are not equal in musical ability and that adjustments to differences are necessary at times. However, it does not follow that the children who maintain the highest and most skillful level of singing ability should be allowed to dominate every singing situation, to the exclusion of the less fortunate of their fellows.

What it does imply is that, in order for every child to use his singing voice more effectively, emphasis will be placed upon the kinds of musical activities that will stimulate and encourage the backward to sing to the best of their ability without fear and without self-consciousness.

A child can be guided to see the need for improving the quality of his voice *after* he has had the experience of singing in the kind of social situations that give meaning to his efforts.

An attempt to teach children to sing in perfect tune with appropriate tone quality by conscious effort is putting the cart before the horse. Furthermore, expecting a child to improve his singing by listening to others until he gets the idea is to deny the principle of interaction in growth and learning. What children take in by listening can have little abiding interest until it is released, shared, and vitalized by the joint singing and rhythmic action of a group.

Normal children learn to sing *by singing*. The big thing when dealing with children who, for any reason whatsoever, are retarded singers is to get singing *going*, rather than too much formality about the order of the going.

To repeat what has been said elsewhere, children have sound instincts about singing. It is something to do, to take pleasure in, and to gain satisfaction from; else there is no joy in it as far as they can see. The freedom to release and express emotions in song results in the kind of joy that Jacques Dalcroze calls a "soul force." This is another way of saying that one of the most valuable outcomes of the joyous singing of children is a sense of freedom joined with responsible action, and children can feel this liberation of spirit in song and dance only when relieved from physical and emotional embarrassment. A pressure of high emotion is generated by the uninhibited collective movement of the song play of children. This can be a powerful force in relieving frustrations and releasing the restraints that hold certain children back, and it is worth thinking about that these blockages may be nothing more spectacular or noteworthy than the interference with a child's perfectly normal impulse and desire to do what others are doing. A child's singing voice is an integral part of his social personality, and it cannot thrive under conditions that leave his gregarious nature unsatisfied.

Good attitudes are as desirable as are good singing voices and in the long run more important to eventual and many-sided musical growth. For favorable reception of (let alone response to) aesthetic experiences, no matter what the area may be, depends largely upon rightness of *emotional* tone

D. Songs for Children

Songs to which children are ready to respond are those that are already singing in their hearts This means songs that are true expressions of the emotions and interests that are the central essence of childhood The songs that feel right to children are those which pulsate with the sounds and movements of the life that they "feel in their bones"

Sentimental or self-conscious poetical and musical comments on life and the universe in general do not belong to the child world

In the child world of today children show the natural tendency of the folk from time immemorial to make music that is direct, sincere, simple, and repetitious in both poetic and tonal-rhythmic content

Songs of this kind sing themselves They include singing games, play songs, counting rhymes, folk songs, a number of patriotic songs and hymns, spirituals, and many beautiful Christmas carols

Age level is unimportant in patriotic songs, hymns, and Christmas carols These are songs beloved by all, old and young alike. This is a wonderful thing, for, from the youngest to the eldest, all can take part.

It is the familiar spirit, rather than actually knowing certain songs, that counts most in the end. This spirit can prevail only when the circumstances surrounding the learning and singing of certain songs are marked by the same informality and freedom that characterize wholesome and happy family life (p. 44, *About Home Folks*).

Singing spontaneously and often with adults and with older boys and girls provides opportunities for young children to gain the feeling of deep, inner satisfaction that comes from being a part of that larger social world toward which they are moving.

This does not mean that the song literature that has its own particular appeal in childhood is to be either neglected or ignored. It is simply this: in the field of music, as in everything else, children live in the child world and the world of adults at one and the same time; and it should be left to the sound instincts of a child's intuitive responses as to how much or how little he will take from the latter.

When choosing children's songs the following are key points:

1. That *elements of familiarity* abound in both music and text.

2. That *range is not too wide.* For inexperienced singers, find songs in which the range does not extend beyond five tones.

3. That *both verbal and musical ideas are presented briefly* in terms which children can understand.

4. That *rhythmic flow has lift and lilt.* This is found usually in simple songs with lightly moving repetitious tonal-rhythmic patterns in which the primary beat is strongly felt.

5. That *music stands on its own feet.* Child interest in subject content, correlative values, even in poetic texts, is secondary. Even in childhood a song lives or dies by the integrity of its musical appeal.

6. That *close correlation occurs between the word sounds and word rhythms and the tonal rhythm of the musical setting of a text.* For example, the word "ding" sounds higher than the word "dong." A song which reverses this order by moving up instead of down on "dong" is doing contrary to what is expected The same thing happens when both the associations and speech rhythms of such words as "skipping" or "running" or "hopping" are sung to a pedestrian pattern of one-beat and two-beat notes. The texts, tunes, and rhythms of songs should combine to intensify the flavor of the tones and rhythms of words as children feel them on their tongues and in their nerves and muscles When this happens, a song has the simple inevitability of images that are already in the bodies, hearts, and minds of children

7 That *melodic content can be grasped as a complete musical*

idea. Tunes of this kind are music to young ears and voices. The chime of rhyme, the jingle of melody, and the lilt of rhythmic movement, which are the essential elements of all song, make a tremendous appeal to children. When songs combine these qualities, they satisfy natural expectations. This is no small matter in the nurture and development of the innate musical tendencies of children.

E. Teaching Songs to Children

The whole matter of *what* and *where* and *when* and *how* to teach songs centers upon seizing and using to advantage every mood and occasion that make children ready to sing.

Children's spontaneous responses to song make it unfortunate when all singing is put aside until that time in the school day which is reserved especially for music.

Young children sing about the pictures they paint, the pets they feed and care for, the stories they hear, the sun that shines and the rain that falls, and they just sing — at odd times, special times, and all times.

Of course it would be impossible, as well as unnecessary, to pick up everything that children do as potential occasions for either creating or learning songs. There are other things besides music which claim the interest and attention of children. A thoughtful teacher, though, does not want to overlook moods and circumstances which can be used to make children more keenly aware of music as another *way of expressing* certain values in their own experience.

For example, a child may come to school full to overflowing because of the advent of a new puppy or kitten; or it might be a *new baby!* His group is with him in spirit. They know just how he feels; the mood is then right for a song that will fit the occasion.

Such incidents happen daily, offering opportunities for teachers to encourage children to sing with an ease that is free of both fear and self-consciousness. In approaches of this kind there is a social motivation that is a strong factor in the nurture of wholesome musical growth.

Children are more sensitive and receptive to a song when they feel the kinship of its tonal-rhythmic patterns to their own moods and experiences. When singing is set aside as a special kind of activity, where songs are taught by formalized steps or routines, children are likely to lose the connection between their everyday affairs and what they get during the music period.

However, this is not to imply that a certain allotted time for music in the school day is unnecessary. Music time, like story time, painting time, or reading time, provides conditions for bringing together and co-ordinating musical experiences that have been present, informally but continually, all day long.

In music attention has to be given to details, to smoothing out rough spots, to dealing with individual needs, to developing better group singing, to enlarging the song repertory, and to correlating singing with an ever-widening range of musical activities.

During the early weeks of the school life of kindergarten and first-grade children, it is a good idea to choose songs that they know and can sing without delay (pp. 38–43, 67–70).

Little children want to sing, and they will sing right along with whoever is singing, whether they know a song or not.

The new songs introduced should be brief, simple, and repetitious in both tune and text, making it easy for children to catch on and join in singing whenever they are ready or wish to do so.

There will be inaccuracies, of course, but in the beginning the spirit of enthusiasm which impels a child to take part is the prime consideration. When children have given expression to their feelings with their own voices, they are ready usually to let the teacher listen while they sing.

Children should hear a more complex song several times before attempting to sing it. But, before concentrating upon isolated figures or phrases, they should be allowed to sing with the teacher as much of the song as they are able. This gives children a feeling for the song as a whole that will make the separate parts more meaningful to them.

Sometimes the unusual order of words in a song will confuse little folks. Usually this clears up when children are given plenty of time, not only to hear both text and tune, but to watch the teacher as she forms words and tones.

At other times unnatural melodic progressions, too many changes in tonal-rhythmic patterns, or too wide a compass of tones may be the seat of the trouble. In such instances it may be wise to drop a song for the time being.

Sometimes teacher-preparation and approach are at fault. Any tension or uncertainty in a teacher's presentation gets a similar response from children. A first requisite for teachers, then, is to know and like the songs which they hope that children, in turn, will learn to know and love. A teacher who is overflowing with the joy of singing never fails to have singing pupils.

F. The Role of the Teacher

The proper realization of all plans for teaching songs and improving the singing voices of children depends on the teacher. Unless a teacher is animated by a sincere belief in children and in their potential capacity for varying degrees of musical development, all the methods and techniques in the world will be of little avail.

It is a great thing for a teacher to be naturally endowed with a good voice. But a greater gift for the teacher is to be able to sympathize with and assist the child who is struggling to improve whatever singing capacity he has to begin with — little or much.

Neither a special teacher of music nor a regular classroom teacher has to be a professional singer. Singing in the schools is no more aimed at making professional performers of boys and girls than teaching the language arts aims to produce actors, orators, radio announcers, or other kinds of public speakers.

However, a good ear for music and a voice that is true, pleasing, and steady are highly desirable. Too much volume and vocal mannerisms, such as tremolos, sustained *crescendos*, prolonged high notes, and other affectations, are positive drawbacks in teaching children to sing. Few things embarrass them more than artificialities and insincerity in any form.

In guiding children to sing with increasing enjoyment, skill, and beauty the following points are worthy of consideration.

1 *Sing for children with directness, simplicity, and enjoyment.* It is a happy experience for children to get into the spirit of a song through the singing of a teacher who enjoys sharing her own love of song with them.

2 *Confidence in oneself is an asset.* No teacher who feels unsure of her own singing can put children at their ease. It is certainly not being overconfident to believe that teachers are as capable of continuous musical growth as are children.

3 *A widely varied and memorized repertory of songs is another asset.* Children like to be looked in the eye by the person who speaks or sings to them. The teacher who wishes to deal with songs and singing just as flexibly and informally as with speech and talking has to be prepared in advance to meet all kinds of diverse moods and situations. For instance, anger or sulkiness can be dispelled in nine cases out of ten when the teacher, looking directly at Johnny or Susie, says, "This is going to be a song about a great big boy (or girl) just like you". To follow this with a song that gives personal recognition at a moment when it is needed requires adequate song resources all ready for use (pp 64–66 with a child's name substituted. In place of "I am" sing "Johnny is," etc.).

4 *Try to capture the unique spirit of each song.* One song may be filled with the lilt of laughter, another may have the gentle tenderness of a lullaby, still another, the vigorous tread of marching feet. Each and every song has mood and quality which the teacher can bring to life for children. Real understanding of a song comes from close attention to its emotional implications. and when songs are interpreted with sympathy and imagination, children rarely fail to respond with appropriate voice quality.

5 *An intelligent and realistic concept of the child voice is a great help.* Observation does not support the theory that the vocal organs of children are fragile and perishable A few moments of listening to the cacophony of children's voices on any playground should banish all doubts concerning the durability of the child voice (p. viii, *The Child Voice*). However, the voice at play is not always the most appropriate for expressive singing; and teachers need to increase their knowledge of what to expect from children at different levels of maturity. At no time should children's voices be overtaxed, nor should loud, harsh, forced, and raucous singing be allowed; neither should children be taught to sing with suppressed voices. Hushed, delicate, and devitalized singing is neither beautiful nor childlike. But when the singing of children is free, vibrant, lilting, and unforced, it is very beautiful indeed.

6. *Careful attention to pitching songs comfortably is important.* Opinions concerning both the pitch and the range of the child voice are changing. Investigation and experiment have shown that the average compass and pitch of the singing tones of young children lie between middle C and fifth-line F on the treble staff and that children acquire self-confidence more readily when singing songs of limited range and comfortable pitch.[1]

7. *Lead or direct the group singing of younger children by suggestion and indirection rather than by overt action.* In the lower grades song-leading in the sense of formal directing is not only unnecessary but undesirable. Even if young children were able to get the significance of conducting techniques, such formalities would take away from the value of singing as a normal, everyday social activity. Leading children into song may be achieved in a variety of ways. At one time the teacher may lead off by singing a phrase or all of a song, to indicate pitch and tempo. At another time the lead may be taken from the piano or from a phonograph record. At still another time a child may be chosen as the leader, to sing for and with his group. When children are at play they tend to "follow their own lead," as well as to be "self-starters" in the matter of singing. These are tendencies for teachers to encourage and guide in nurturing the musical initiative of children

8 *Use the pitch pipe and piano with judgment.* The pitch pipe has value for teachers. Whether experienced or otherwise, the teacher who is learning new material away from the piano will find it a great convenience; and for those whose ears cannot be trusted, a pitch pipe should be used as a frequent check at the end as well as at the beginning of a song The piano can be invaluable for teaching as well as accompanying songs. But in neither instance is it good to employ a piano as either a substitute for or a dominating factor in children's singing. Too much

[1] *The Music of Young Children*, Gladys Moorhead and Donald Pond I, Chant Pillsbury Foundation Studies, 1941 Santa Barbara, California
"A Study of the Development of Children's Ability to Sing," Jersild and Bienstock *Journal of Educational Psychology*, October, 1934.
There's Music in Children, Emma D Sheehy Chapter 3, "Singing." Henry Holt and Company, 1946

piano can dull the ear, devitalize the voice, and weaken independent singing On the other hand, the piano wisely used can quicken ears, awaken imagination, enliven and give color to singing, and stimulate musical interest and initiative The piano (played by the teacher), the phonograph, and the radio should not be thought of as providing music that is over and above the singing, playing, and creative efforts of children, but as additional enrichment in a continually expanding range of musical activities and experiences.

II · Rhythmic Expression

A. Rhythmic Response in Children

There is no such thing as separating rhythmic activity from the countless pursuits which engage the interest and attention of children. Children pulsate with rhythmic energy. Their entire beings are keyed to respond to recurrent beat, to regular and irregular accents, and to the thousand and one variations of long and short, fast and slow.

There is plenty of visible evidence to support the theory that these responses are animated by vital forces, both within and without, that move children to experiment endlessly with their own physical capacity for rhythmic expression.

Play in childhood is essentially rhythmic. It progresses from action merely for the sake of being active to movement that is turned to expressive purposes. This indicates that emotion and imagination are deeply involved in forming together in a child's mind an increasing number of meaningful associations between his sensory impressions and the sound and movement patterns of his play.

The infinite number of varied and complex activities which children devise during playtime is their way of accumulating, co-ordinating, and using as many ideas, learnings, and controls as they can manage to crowd into their waking hours.

Music is an integral part of learning the play way, for spontaneous singing and rhythmic expression are simultaneous with most of the physical activity of childhood. Furthermore, nearly all physical motion may be related in some way to the rhythmic content of the music.

It should not be forgotten, however, that the physical approach provides only a beginning to the rhythm of music in its highest reaches. For example, a Beethoven Scherzo embodies rhythmic concepts that are freed from the limitations of the human body.

Be that as it may, the child approach to the rhythmic content of music is in physical expression. A child who is clapping the beat of a song or running and stamping to a piece played on the piano or phonograph is gaining a finer sense of the expressive values of his own rhythmic movements.

Motor responses in relation to singing, listening, and playing create in children a sense of balance and freedom that leads to self-realization, which is the principal purpose of both play and music in the education of young children.

The spontaneous, unsupervised play of children provides teachers with indications that will help them to determine the natural activities from which learned rhythmic responses are developed.

Progress in broadening the interests and increasing powers of control will be more sure when children can see ideal values in relation to their own experiences and purposes See pages 10–12, "Running" (Children's Song), "Run, Run, Run" (Concone), and "Running Game" (Gurlitt).

B. Free Rhythmic Play

The free, uninhibited, and untaught rhythmic actions of children are virtually unlimited in scope and variety. Running and walking, skipping and tripping, trotting and galloping, hopping and jumping, pushing and pulling, bending and stretching, reaching and grasping, swinging and swaying, patting and stroking, beating and banging, rising and falling, creeping and crawling, twisting and turning, rolling and tumbling—these are only a beginning of basic themes upon which children improvise endless variations.

The urge to run, jump, slide, etc., is often carried on for the pure pleasure of "letting go." It is a joyous and exhilarating experience for children to *feel* the freedom of their bodies as they cover and explore space. Since space itself is a stimulus to movement, it is desirable for children to have plenty of room for rhythmic activities.

A quickened emotion and a liberated imagination are present when children discover, by their own experimental movements, the meaning of such spatial relations as up and down, round and round, in and out, back and forth, and so on.

It is equally stimulating for them to get concepts of fast and slow, long and short, heavy and light, in terms of physical action.

These and other simple and direct responses to rhythmic movement are experimental tryouts that prepare children to deal, later on, with more complex factors of rhythm as it applies to both physical expression and musical motion. They help children also to co-ordinate sensory perceptions with accompanying and resultant motions and emotions.

A still more important value is that free, inventive rhythmic-tonal expression integrates motor and aural, visual and kinesthetic images by actual physical affirmations which children feel from head to foot.

Guidance and suggestions from teachers are indispensable for both the recognition and the development of the permanent values that grow out of the elementary activities of free rhythmic play.

Children have to be helped to see even the immediate possibilities of their play rhythms in relation to the songs they sing, the instruments they play, and the music they hear on a piano or a phonograph.

Even greater is their need for guidance in building up a background of associations and images that will open up an ever-widening range of musical interests and purposes.[1]

When children learn to apply their familiar play movements to the rhythmic patterns of their school music experiences, they come into a fuller realization of what they have already experienced many times and in many ways (pp. 38–43, *About Playing Games*).

Children *sense* unity, balance, and climax in so simple a sequence of expressive actions as "turning round and round, turning round and round" until the climax of "then all fall down" is reached (p. 38, "Ring-Around a Rosy").

In younger years the balance of sequences that do "now this, now that" or go "this way and that way" is likely to be outweighed by the excitement of such a high point as jumping up, clapping hands above heads, and crying, "Whoops!" as in "Sally Go Round the Stars" (p. 39). But things are likely to fall into their right places *if* children are given enough preparatory experience with songs and games that allow for and invite climactic sound and rhythmic effects. Children are full of inventiveness in this respect, and they should be given opportunities for initiating rhythmic activities of their own. In these instances musical accompaniments would follow the lead of the children instead of children's always interpreting "what the music says."

Simple percussion instruments are recommended for both pupil and teacher use. Children can use a drum, a bell, or a wood-block either to accompany or to initiate rhythmic patterns. A triangle usually suggests a light tiptoe run, while drums indicate slow, heavy walking or a quick-step march. Duration, volume, accents, tempo, and mood are felt and responded to more directly and more freely when the accompanying instrument is not only easy to manipulate but close kin to clapping hands, snapping fingers, tapping feet, and moving bodies. (See page 137, *About Other Things That Sing*.)

All these things count in a child's responses to the

[1]*Education for Musical Growth*, James L. Mursell, Chapter 3. Ginn and Company, 1948.

rhythms and sounds that come to him from every side. Children are at home in the world of moving sound and they make use of its patterns, either combined or separately. Both are media of expression inseparable from play itself and are as natural to children as breathing.

C. Imitative Play

It is not possible to draw a line of demarcation between the free, imitative, and dramatic play of children. All are ways that the young have of "acting themselves out" into more meaningful relations with a brand-new and wonderful world. A child's responses are lively, and he senses much about the people and things in his environment. However, he doesn't rest with this; but he deepens and clarifies his impressions by imitating what he sees, hears, and feels.

So we find a child running, not only for the fun of running, but running to get on the inside of all creatures and things that run. In the beginning of his explorations he may say, "See, I can run like a truck!" but in no time at all he is a truck, and he proceeds to prove it in convincing movement and sound.

The child's way of affirming his feeling of kinship for anything and everything that appeals to his interest is to be as much like a given person or thing as possible, and to children nothing is impossible. They will cleave the air like gulls one minute and crawl over the floor like tractors the next. What they choose to imitate, or rather *to be*, is a matter of complete impartiality.

The big policeman on the school corner, an airplane in the sky, a duck waddling to the pond, an elephant in a circus parade, the wind blowing, and many, many other people, creatures, and things—all invite his observation and impersonation.

Expressive activity of this kind is essentially rhythmic, and it gains unity, clarity, and deeper meaning when related to appropriate musical experiences.

Imitative play and music just naturally go together.

Children can't "play like" trains without singing "ding-dongs," "toot-toots," "all-aboards," and "choo-choos." When encouraged and guided, this primitive form of dramatic play opens up a wide field for creative activity of all sorts. (See pages xvii–xix, *Creative Expression*.) Furthermore, it gives a tremendous lift to shy, backward, and inexperienced singers. (See pages viii–xi, *Individual Differences in Children's Singing*.)

Children forget themselves in their identification with what they impersonate, leaving imaginations and voices free to do quite amazing things.

Who can say which comes first, the rhythmic mimicry that evokes chanting and singing, or the songs and melodies that make movements freer and more expressive? In any case, all go together in the lives of children, overlapping and crisscrossing to give experience a richer texture of associations and meanings.

D. Dramatic Play

Dramatic play is nothing more or less than an extension (and a corollary) of free and imitative play. Making "a play" of a song or an instrumental piece is not a new phase of either social or musical experience. Children don't have to "learn how" to do this. They just go on being a given character (Handy Spandy, who loved plum-cake and sugar candy, p. 70, or the mother who "spanked her little daughter for spoiling her nice new clothes," p. 70), instead of being taught how to act a part in a play.

Dramatic interpretations should be nothing more special or stylized than free and imitative play. Dramatizing a song, however, is an extension of these activities that calls for an expansion of ideas, as well as the control of individual action in relation to parts played by others. Furthermore, synchronizing expressive physical actions with singing or instrumental selections demands concentrated and co-ordinated effort, which, in turn, contributes to musical discrimination.

Because of these things it is advisable for children to move gradually from class-wide imitative play and impersonations to dramatizations that call for a cast of characters.

An entire group can dramatize in unison "Little Jack Horner" (p. 68), or "Here Is the Beehive" (p. 37), or "Two Little Birds" (p. 36), with each child giving "the act" his own individual interpretation.

But thought, planning, and co-operation are necessary when undertaking songs as short and simple even as are "Two Little Kitty-Cats" (p. 112), "Mrs. Hen and Little Chick" (p. 115), and "Six Little Mice" (p. 117). The thought and effort required to see "The Little Red Hen" (p. 159) and "Nocturne" (p. 74) through to the end demands sustained concentration that should not be forced on children before they are ready.

Graceful movements and the precision of controlled techniques are neither the immediate purpose nor the final aim of dramatic play. In relation to music its principal function is to provide another way for children to discover and to make more effective use of their individual gifts in group undertakings.

Both social and musical values are greatly enhanced when they are derived from imaginative interpretations which are *comments in action*, so to speak, that children make about music.

These *comments*, if unstudied, will be rhythmic, though undramatic in the usual sense of the word. But when the dramatic play of children is direct and sincere, the effect is always touchingly simple and sweet.

Songs and instrumental selections suitable for dramatic interpretations are:

Songs

For *About Playing Games*, see pages 38–43.
For *Finger and Toe Games*, see pages 49–51.
Both are elementary forms of pantomime and dramatic play that are universally beloved by children.

Instrumental Selections

E. Apparatus, Materials, and Properties

Children are responsive to color as well as tone, and to tactile sensations as well as to rhythmic movement. They have also an insatiable desire to touch, handle, manipulate, and control everything they can get their hands on.

These impulses and responses can be turned to advantage in music, particularly in connection with rhythmic activities. Balls and hoops, jumping ropes and swings, scooters and seesaws, skates and doll-buggies, slides and jungle-jims, to mention only a few things, are closely related to children's play, and therefore to their play songs (pp. 29–32).

Whether this kind of apparatus or play material is used actually or imaginatively, the familiar action patterns, set to music, can help children to develop greater freedom and ease of rhythmic expression.

In imitative and dramatic play, actually having tops, toy trains and planes, stick-horses, doll-buggies and cradles, and other playthings will often make a self-conscious and diffident child forget himself (pp. 127–135).

Scarves and balloons delight children for a number of reasons. They supply the charm of color; they are nice to touch; and they are exciting to manipulate, for their visual movements and forms make a strong appeal to the imagination.

A balloon waved back and forth by its string, in time to music, sometimes has a magical effect on a child who has been indifferent to other types of rhythmic play. Balloons, when free of attached strings or sticks, can be tossed up, then kept in the air by lightly touching with the finger tips. Slow waltz rhythms are good for activities of this type (p. 31).

Varicolored scarves of diaphanous material appeal even more than balloons to the emotions and imaginations of children. Besides the color and texture—and both are pleasing—a variety of rhythmic improvisations are inspired by the beautiful visual patterns that scarves can make.

For instance, scarves can fly, float and flutter, whirl, swirl, and ripple with the effortless grace of winging birds; they can flap like sails or trail with stately majesty.

Then scarves are fun for children to experiment with in dozens of ways. One group of children was observed rolling up in them like cocoons. As they unwound, the teacher played a drum roll. At another time they covered themselves with scarves draped lengthwise over their heads, then moved about with stiff, staccato steps to a rhythm tapped out on a tone block.

For activities such as those described above, the length of a scarf should be double the height of a child. This makes a scarf long enough for playing birds, butterflies,— and angels!

For making wings, run a scarf sash-wise under the arms and single-tie it in the back. With arms outspread a child catches and holds lightly between thumb and fore-finger the upper corner of each end of his scarf. He then has wings that will flutter and fold, spread and dip, etc.

Used lengthwise, a scarf makes a fine train for playing kings and queens. Add a paper crown, and the costume is complete enough for the grandest ceremonial march (pp. 25–28).

Scarves can't be makeshift. Inexpensive materials in different colors are available. In case the colors are un-satisfactory, cold-water dyes come in gorgeous shades.

A final word about taking care of scarves. A number of teachers have the children roll their scarves up, then stuff them into a string shopping bag that is hung in a closet. Besides being simpler than folding, the crinkly effect caused by wadding and crushing is very attractive.

Children are never at a loss for ideas when it comes to adaptable materials and properties which capture their interest.

Children also love to "dress up," and a costume chest doesn't necessarily involve expense. Cast-off curtains and draperies, as well as wraps, hats, and the like, will surely be contributed by families and friends once a group of children get the collecting mania.

III · Creative Expression

Creative expression in music is not an activity that can be set apart from other types of musical growth and learning. Nor does the fostering of creative musical growth require conditions that are different from those provided for other lines of musical development.

Therefore each phase and every aspect of a widely varied and comprehensive program of music education contribute to the nurture of creative musical growth. Singing and rhythmic movement, listening and playing instruments, free and dramatic rhythmic play, all call for expressive responses that are essentially creative. Fur-thermore, these activities provide a background of per-sonal, social, and musical experiences without which there would be little for children to draw upon for spontaneous expression. And the basic purposes of creative musical activities are to develop keener sensibilities and to stimu-late and encourage a wider spread of musical initiative among children.

Sensitizing children to the qualities of experience in general and to music in particular is not a difficult matter. Children's senses are as eager to taste the flavors of life as their growing bodies are hungry to be fed.

Young children literally put out "feelers" to reach for, catch, and pull into themselves all the tastes and smells, sights and sounds, movements and textures that they can hold or endure.

The sound of falling rain, a fire siren, the swish of trees in the wind, the screech of brakes; the sight of water sparkling in the sun, of a silver plane flashing in the sky,

of an arching rainbow, of trees in bloom; the touch of mud and gravel between the toes, the silky smoothness of a kitten's fur or of a rose petal on lips or tongue—these and thousands of other sensory impressions are food for im-aginative growth and expression. And these are experi-ences that tell children things about themselves and their world that can never be put into books.

A first important step, then, in developing creative growth in little children is to keep alive and to help them to realize the value of tasting life to the full: opening ears and eyes to an increasing perception of color, interest, variety, and beauty of sight and sound, touch and taste, space and movement; and warming the hearts and freeing expressive personalities to feel and to do more; therefore to be and to know more.

Since children are naturally responsive to tones and rhythms, they seize music as another way of groping toward the discovery of themselves and their world. Children sense singing and dancing as acts of exuberant vitality. Their zest for life makes even the practical busi-ness of getting to school in the morning a delightful ad-venture. They have discovered music as a medium of physical and vocal expression in which they can catch and project some of their most ecstatic experiences.

Children sing, dance, and chant to re-create their feel-ings for every moving experience, from going to the store to things "east of the sun and west of the moon." Even in childhood fleeting glimpses of some lovely or poignant aspect of a simple, ordinary thing or event can be translated into and frequently transmuted by musical expression.

As would be expected, however, the "make-up" songs of children tend to center around identifying themselves with animals, things, people, and natural phenomena (p. 63, *About Folks We Like to Know*; p. 93, *About the Wonderful Outside World*; p. 137, *About Other Things That Sing*).

Children are following deep-seated instincts when they strive to sustain sensation until it reaches the stage of creative reproduction and interpretation.

Making up a song that projects what a child feels about the way a tugboat, or a sailboat, or the milkman's horse, or an elephant, or the coal man, or a streamlined train sounds and moves is, at his level, a highly creative act. It is the child's method of forming a connecting link between *some thing* as it actually exists apart from himself and his personal interpretation of what it means to him (p. xv, *Imitative Play*).

In *being* whatever it is he gains further insight into its essential quality, be it man or beast, natural phenomena or mechanical device. But this quest for an enlarging background of associations and meanings should extend further than creative action on the child level can go without enrichment from what the culture has to offer.

For instance, a little boy may make up a song about an elephant, or he may create a rhythmic pattern on a deep-toned drum that goes "the way an elephant walks." The experience will take on a broader significance for him, as well as for his group, if all listen to and interpret music that is relevant to the spontaneous expression of the child (p. 121, "March," by Hollaender).

Another instance with another kind of extension of associations was observed in a kindergarten. A severe rainstorm came up, much to the interest of the children. As they looked on with a great deal of excited comment and stirring about, suddenly, as if by some commonly understood but wordless signal, they began to chant:

As it went on and on the teacher took a homemade maraca from the instrument shelf and shook it in rhythm with feet and hands that were already keeping time.

Several children followed the teacher's lead, the additional instruments giving more body to the accompaniment. Almost at once the tempo of the chant quickened, with a rising *crescendo* of tone that reached a climax, then gradually died away. The storm was over.

The children themselves had created a mood that was right for listening quietly to a record which the teacher placed on the phonograph without comment (p. 115, "Etincelles").

When it had finished, a little *girl* said, "That music sounded like the rain looked when the sun shined through it."

This started a series of sentence songs, children singing what they felt, saw, or heard, voluntarily and with complete lack of self-consciousness. The teacher interposed no suggestions beforehand concerning selection of topics, choice of words, or rhyme schemes. Nor did she dull the fresh charm of the children's naïve little songs with attention to the formalities and practical routines of musical structure.

From this it should not be inferred that the grammar of musical structure is considered unimportant. It is merely that first things have to come first in the expressive development of little children. In the beginning of their creative musical experiences the first and all-important point is that they have *something to say*; the second, that they are at liberty to sing, dance, play, or speak what they feel without being hampered by restricting formalities that as yet have no significance for them.

Once children are filled with a desire to express and they are given the choice of many ways in which to use their creative energies, regard for refinements of organization and aesthetic qualities of media and presentation will follow in due time.

Expression is all of a piece with children, and their unpremeditated music-making is characterized by short lengths,—or brevity of concept. This is the only possible way for a child to encompass and formulate his musical ideas with any reasonable degree of clarity. It is futile with young children to attempt to isolate the essential elements of expression, as if they were separate ingredients in the total of an expressive act. *Form*, for example, in either a verbal or a musical sentence, is not, to a child, something apart from his idea, but is an integral and distinguishing aspect of the feeling that he is trying to share.

A two-year-old who says:

> "I want a kitty,
> A kitty with pink feet,
> A kitty with pink hands,
> A kitty with pink hair,
> But blue eyes like me."

is expressing herself with the unstudied charm and simple grace of direct and unelaborate childhood. Brief in statement and simple in structure, but colored by the delight which all young children take in anything that touches their hearts.

A small girl was seen dancing her way to school with movements as lilting and free as those of a winging bird. All her delight in wind-blown clouds and bright dashes of rain was poured into what was, to her, a love song to the world:

> "I love the wind,
> I love the rain;
> O lovely wind,
> O lovely rain,
> I'm glad,
> I'm glad,
> I'm glad you came."

Experiences of this kind do not contribute directly to improving manipulative skill, to adding to power of invention, to increasing analytical ability; nor do they always *inform* the mind. The creative function of the ingenuous musical expressions of childhood goes deeper. Theirs is to *form* the child, heart as well as body, spirit as well as mind, all being one and indivisible. Whether the creative activity is spontaneous or whether it is recreative in the sense of stimulating imaginative responses to singing, listening, or playing on instruments, each contributes to giving direction and refinement to the developing musical personalities of childhood.

Providing the tools, skills, and knowledge for children to use in creative musical expression is neither the first nor the basic consideration. Stress, first, last, and always, should be placed upon growing, active children and their natural zest for life. This gives them a special craving to express moods which they do not know how to put into words. Very young boys and girls feel deep down inside themselves that music helps them to understand as well as to enjoy life. Furthermore, they know that making up songs and dances and pieces to play is not a duty, but a joyful experience in self-discovery. And the golden key of creative growth is self-discovery that leads out into continually expanding and richer areas of fulfilling experiences.

IV · Listening to Music

Aural perception, or listening, is inherent in each phase of every activity that contributes to musical growth.

There could be no singing, no physical response to tonal-rhythmic patterns, no playing upon instruments, no appreciation of the literature of music, without the capacity to hear and respond to tonal design.

Good listening is far from being an act of passive reception. On the contrary it is an active use of mind and imagination in following and responding to ideas that are expressed in moving patterns of tone.

Listening to music with increasing sensitivity to tone and insight into tonal relations is a capacity that is gradually developed in children through their active participation in diverse and varied musical experiences.

Communication in the language of music, similar to that in the language arts, is a two-way process: hearing and interpreting, responding and expressing. Expressive images and patterns of both speech and music can become familiar and useful only when continually heard and applied in experiences that give them vitality and meaning.

In essence the capacity to get what is said in either music or speech arts depends, to a large extent, upon good thinking; and good thinking in dealing with tonal relationships requires a mind well filled with meaningful musical imagery, or else the listener has little to draw upon in reference to what is new and unfamiliar.

It is said that children have to talk themselves into thinking. Correspondingly they have to sing, dance, and play themselves into an inner hearing of the aural images that form the matter of musical thought.

Like every other step forward in musical growth, appreciative listening is the outcome of self-testing in action. Children are not ready to *think* music until they have acquired a fund of tonal-rhythmic images by *acting out* or objectifying their responses to what music has to say to them. Through singing, rhythmic play, and playing instruments, good listeners are being developed gradually and continually.

To reiterate, listening is one of the features of a closely co-ordinated and carefully guided program of varied, extensive, and unbroken musical experiences. Consequently there should be no division of aims and purposes between what goes on in listening-time and what happens when children sing, play instruments, create music, and express themselves in rhythmic action.

It is merely that conditions for quiet listening are different, and there should always be some time set aside for children to listen to music with a quietness of body that leaves them freer for mental and imaginative activity.

It is a step forward, too, for children to go from the realities of their own active experiences into the more idealized forms of music that can be heard on the piano, phonograph, radio, and at concerts.

While children differ in both the breadth and depth of their musical interests, there are, nevertheless, certain attitudes and responses that are fairly constant in young children. These should be determining factors in choosing materials and in providing conditions that will increase their enjoyment of listening to music. Briefly summarized they are:

A. Conditions

1. Physical comfort and a friendly and happy emotional atmosphere are necessary. Music can then have a chance to be *felt* as well as heard.

2. Varied approaches and procedures help. Quiet listening is desirable from the teacher's standpoint, and children can achieve it up to a certain point under certain conditions. Variety is one. Attention span is short, and desire for action is long. If little children fidget about and make audible comments, it is only natural. They are not audiences either by preference or by nature. Make as many occasions as possible for children to take part: hum a melody, clap a rhythm, make comments, and ask questions.

3. *The example of the teacher.* This is far and away the most influential factor in conditioning children to sensitive and discriminative listening. A phonograph or a radio is merely an instrumentality. Neither can operate independently in conveying the values of music to children. This makes it all the more necessary for listening responses to be intensely alive; else what fills the ears will have no chance to penetrate into the heart and mind. Effective listening is induced by the example the teacher sets. When a teacher attends to the music that is played with all her heart and her entire mind, the children feel it, and their responses are likely to be lively and imaginative. But when the teacher's mind wanders or she feels uncertain, children become both indifferent and inattentive. A teacher, then, who is filled with the wonder and beauty of a singing world will provide conditions for listening to music that will help to quicken and deepen the sense of life and wonderment that is so characteristic of little children. And this is the real purpose of all art and all appreciation.

B. Kinds of Music Children Like

1. *Familiar melodies*—instrumental arrangements of songs that children know should be provided. Children are responsive to melodies and rhythms that can be associated with their own familiar world, resulting in such comments as "That sounds like rain falling" (p. 11) or comments of similar nature.

2. *Melodies that are simple and songlike* in the instrumental pieces that they listen to. Tunes that children can hum and sing make a friendly connection between their own singing voices and the "voice" of a violin, or flute, or a *tuba!* ("Tubby the Tuba" has made this instrument a familiar friend.) Suggested numbers:

> Dance of the Happy Spirits, p. 34
> Lullaby, p. 61
> Valse Gracieuse, p. 97
> Waltz (Brahms), p. 31
> Papillons No. 8, p. 108

3. *Music that has sheer beauty of tone.* Children are highly susceptible to tone, to the feel of it as it falls on the ear. They respond to the loveliness of a beautifully played string or wind tone with the same pleasure that they get from stroking velvet or a kitten's fur. This kind of musical beauty is usually found in extended works, but a teacher can learn to stop a record at an eighth or a sixteenth measure cadence (period or full stop). Eight bars, for example, from Bach's "Air for G String"; sixteen bars from the Andante of Haydn's "Clock Symphony"; or sixteen bars of the Nocturne from Mendelssohn's "Midsummer Night's Dream." The full meaning of these and similar pieces would be over the heads of little folks,

but not the beauty of tone itself when selections are presented in abbreviated form.

4. *Music that is strongly suggestive of moods.* Feeling response to music is marked in children. Many of their deepest joys are experienced in moments of grave fascination. They have also their lighter moods, for children are people; therefore they are subject to as many changes of and responses to mood as are other normal people. (Children cannot put into words the feeling that they have for music, but their responses to the mood of music are no less real and enduring.) The following are examples of distinctive moods:

> Dance of the Happy Spirits, p. 34 (serenely quiet)
> Resting Time, p. 35 (quiet and dreamy)
> Cradle Song, p. 59 (tender and comforting)
> Lullaby, p. 61 (gentle and enfolding)
> Birdling, p. 107 (happy and carefree)
> Dance, Dolly, Dance, p. 129 (gay and playful)
> Gnomes, p. 75 (mischievous and frolicsome)
> Nocturne, p. 74 (strange and mysterious)

5. *Music that has rhythmic vitality.* Children not only get a sense of liveliness and well-being from rhythmic music, but they recognize its kinship to their own moods and purposes. (See pages 8–32; 46–61; 100–108.) Examples of fine contrasts in both motion and mood are found in:

> Let's Take a Walk, p. 23 (easygoing and friendly)
> Walking, p. 24 (lingering and pensive)
> Air de Ballet, p. 24 (stately and solemn)
> Military March, p. 26 (prancing and lighthearted)
> The Tin Soldiers Marching, p. 28 (bumpy and jolly)
> Soldiers' March (*Faust*), p. 28 (swinging and bold)

6. *Story music.* Children love stories of every kind and form, provided they deal with something that they know about and can follow. First of all, music of this kind should be good music, regardless of program or narrative associations. Second, story music should be short and to the point; else it is likely to be confusing. Children need to be on familiar ground; otherwise they feel at a disadvantage. A narrative in tone, like any other story, pleases children most when they can anticipate what is coming next. A good example of simple story music is "Riding a Stick-Horse," p. 57.

Children like to make their own stories about what the music says to them. This should be encouraged so long as interpretations are relevant to the music. Other examples of story music:

Nocturne, p. 74	In a Bird Store, p. 107
Gnomes, p. 75	The Tame Bear, p. 122
Legend of the Bells, p. 91	Bear-Dance, p. 122
Nature's Dream, p. 104	

ABOUT FOLKS

Tommy and Sammy and
    Betty and Sue,
Playing and growing the
    Whole day through.

Mothers and Daddies and
    Grandmothers too,
And sweet little babies who
    Frolic and coo.

Postmen and milkmen and
    Candy-men too;
But what about me and
    What about you?

             L. B. P.

What About Me?

Lots of other children[1]
All around me,
But they aren't me.

They haven't got my mother,
They haven't got my daddy,
And they aren't me.

Margaret Wise Brown

A child begins musical expression by giving voice to the way he feels about "me" and "myself"—inside and out. Songs that children make up and sing to themselves are usually expressions of personal feelings urgently in need of satisfying outlets.

However, personal uses of music are fairly balanced, even in early childhood, with song-dance as a means of social interchange. This is observed in the many natural ways that children have of going from "me" to "you"— "I've told you about 'me.' What about you?" "My name is George Brown. What is your name?" "I am five years old. How old are you?" and so on.

Then children, from infancy on, enjoy singing greetings: "Hello," "Bye-bye," and "How do you do?" Also greetings for special occasions take on added importance when given musical settings. Some of the qualities of ritual enter when "Happy Birthday" and "Merry Christmas" are sung.

These amenities, when associated with singing, have the value also of combining the social and musical development of young children at a time when all things come together. (Furthermore these musical and social learnings will be more effective because they are more enjoyable when children and grown-ups sing and dance and play song games together.)

Learning to sing is like learning to talk. A child acquires a useful vocabulary in each of these languages through associations with those more experienced than himself.

Home, neighborhood, and school provide children with the kind of social life that is stimulating to both expression and response. And the way that other people respond to a child's instinctive and unformed efforts either to talk or to sing is of equal importance with the child's responses to what he sees and hears from the people about him.

A Song About Me

Lady Bell

From "Singing Circle"

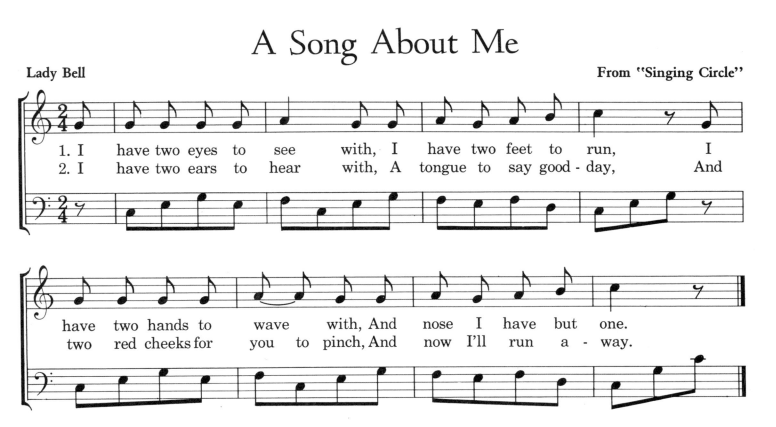

1. I have two eyes to see with, I have two feet to run, I
2. I have two ears to hear with, A tongue to say good-day, And

have two hands to wave with, And nose I have but one.
two red cheeks for you to pinch, And now I'll run a-way.

[1]Taken from *Another Here and Now Story Book*, edited by Lucy Sprague Mitchell, published
and copyright 1937 by E. P. Dutton & Co., Inc., New York.

3

There was a boy, a tiny mite,
Who tried to fly a mighty kite,
And then, alas!
It came to pass
Both boy and kite flew out of sight.

L. Frank Baum

Would You Like to Know?

L.B.P.

Amanda Langland

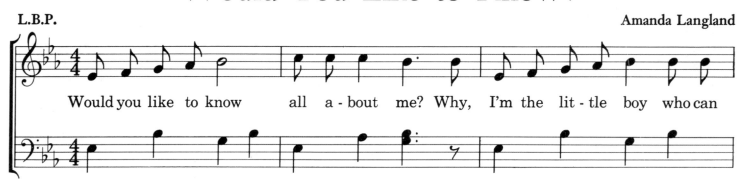

Would you like to know all a-bout me? Why, I'm the lit-tle boy who can

climb that big tall tree! Would you like to know what I

found up there, A-way at the top? A big ripe pear!

Who Are You?

German Folk Tune

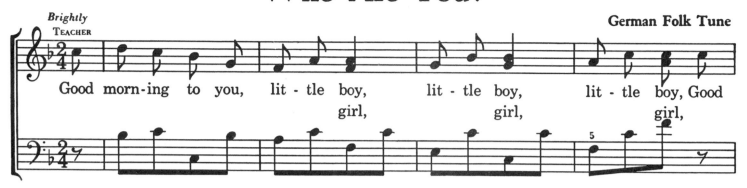

Brightly

TEACHER

Good morn-ing to you, lit - tle boy, lit - tle boy, lit - tle boy, Good
girl, girl, girl,

PUPIL

morn-ing to you, lit - tle boy, who are you? I am John.
girl, (sing your name.) Jane.

The names used below will assist you in helping a pupil to fit his own name to his melodic answer.

I am Ma - rie. I am Pe - ter. I am The - o - dore.
Je - rome. Ma - ry. Is - a - belle.

I am An - to - ni - o. I am Al - ex - an - der.
Do - min - i - ca. Ju - li - an - a.

I'm five years old and like to wear
A bow of ribbon on my hair.
Sometimes it's pink, sometimes it's blue;
I think it's pretty there, don't you?

Unknown

5

When people say, "If I were YOU,"
And tell me what I ought to do,
I often wonder what they'd say
If it turned out that I was THEY.

If I was anyone but ME,
Of course I know that it might be
Not quite so nice, and rather strange,
And so I think I will not change.

John Drinkwater

Everybody Says

Dorothy Aldis

Marian Major

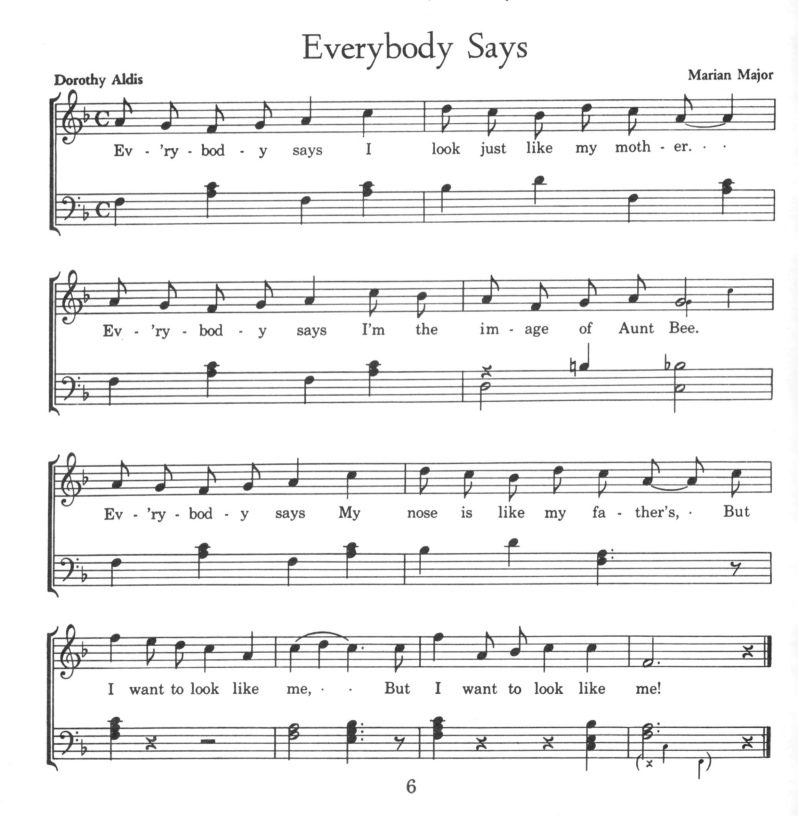

Ev - 'ry - bod - y says I look just like my moth - er. . .

Ev - 'ry - bod - y says I'm the im - age of Aunt Bee.

Ev - 'ry - bod - y says My nose is like my fa - ther's, · But

I want to look like me, · · But I want to look like me!

6

My Bed

Elizabeth Manson Scott[1]

Paul Forde

1. I have a lit-tle bed, Just for me. Broth-er is too big for it,
2. I have a lit-tle bed, Do you see? Pus-sy is too small for it,

Mum-my is too big for it, Dad-dy is too big for it, Do you see?
Pup-py is too small for it, Ba-by is too small for it, It's just for me.

My Zipper Suit

Mary Louise Allen

Sue Hanlin

1. My zip-per suit is bun-ny brown, The top zips up, the
2. My dad-dy brought it out from town, Zzzzzzzzzip it up, zzzzzzz-

legs zip down, I wear it ev-'ry day.
zip it down, And hur-ry out to play.

[1]Taken from *Another Here and Now Story Book*, edited by Lucy Sprague Mitchell, published and copyright 1937 by E. P. Dutton & Co., Inc., New York.

Singing While We Play

The world's a very happy place
Where every child should dance and sing,
And always have a smiling face,
And never sulk for anything.

The world is such a happy place
That children, whether big or small,
Should always have a smiling face,
And never, never sulk at all.

Gabriel Setoun

Play is the child's way of learning as well as of growing. It is obvious that play is not play to children unless accompanied by sound and movement. When listening to and observing children at play, one's ears are filled with clashes of tone that match what the eyes see: a continual crisscross of rhythmic movement.

Closer attention to what this or that group are engaged in at a given moment indicates that whatever children do in the way of repetitious movement is usually accompanied by chanting, rhyming, or singing. It does not matter whether it is the rolling and tumbling of small children or their digging, patting, smoothing and sifting motions in a sand pile; or it may be stepping, trotting, galloping, or skipping just for fun; or it might be climbing steps, going down slides, or one of the many other things that children delight to do—any and all are rhythmic.

Rhythmic motions, once they are caught up and repeated by a group of children, are invariably intensified in song or some other form of vocal expression.

The songs provided at this point follow the play patterns of children. In fact, many were taken down while watching groups of youngsters at play.

It follows that the group should have the fun of physically expressing the actions suggested in the texts of these songs. Since children go into action with so much vigor and enthusiasm, it may be expedient to have one group sing while the others run, skip, and jump!

The important role of the piano and phonograph in stimulating and encouraging active rhythmic expression cannot be overemphasized.

See page xiv, *Free Rhythmic Play*; page xv, *Imitative Play*.

Will You Come and Play?

Adapted from an old American Game Song

Will you come, oh, will you come, Will you come and play to-day?
We can run and skip and hide, We can jump and swing and slide.

Will you come, oh, will you come, Will you come and play?

For running and skipping music see pages 10–17.

8

Come Along

L.B.P.

Folk Tune

Come a - long and join our sing-ing, Come a - long and join our song, Tir - a -

lir - a - lir - a - lir - a, Tir - a - lir - a is our song.

Warm Hands

English Folk Song

1. Warm hands now,   men are gone to plow;
2. Clap, clap, hold,   clap - ty, clap - ty, hold.

If you want to warm your hands, just warm your hands now.
Clap - ty, clap - ty, clap - ty, clap - ty, clap - ty, clap, hold.

1. Pretend to warm hands that are cold.
2. Clap while singing words that fit the rhythmic pattern:

Clap, clap, hold, clap - ty, clap - ty, hold.

Clap - ty, clap - ty, clap - ty, clap - ty, clap - ty, clap, hold.

3. Vary activity by (a) tapping with fingers or rhythm sticks; (b) ringing bells; (c) jingling jingle sticks; (d) shaking tambourines; (e) beating drums.

9

Clapping and Stamping

F.S.

Frances Shaughnessey

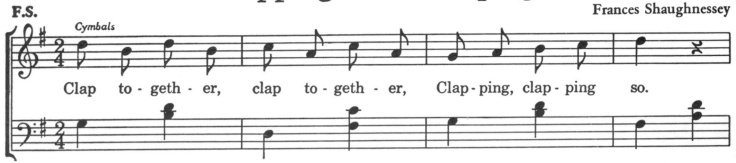

Clap to-geth-er, clap to-geth-er, Clap-ping, clap-ping so.

Stamp-ing, stamp-ing, stamp-ing, stamp-ing, Stamp-ing as we go.

This may be accompanied by cymbals and drums. See page xiv, *Free Rhythmic Play.*

Running

Children's Song

Run-ning up and run-ning down, We're run-ning up and run-ning down, We're

run-ning up and run-ning down, We're run-ning, run-ning all a-round.

This is good for imitative play.

Children will enjoy running like a pony, a dog, a chicken, a robin, and other creatures and doing things which the children themselves will suggest.

See page xv, *Imitative Play.*

Run, Run, Run!

Giuseppe Concone

Free Play: Running quickly and lightly; circling and whirling; clapping hands, tapping fingers, etc.

Imitative Play: Running like a turkey, a robin, or a chicken; frolicking like squirrels or kittens; making hands or feet patter like rain.

(Victor Rhythm Album Two.)

Song of the Shepherdess

Carl Maria von Weber

Free Play: Running with springing steps; running on tiptoes; circling and whirling; clapping.
Imitative Play: Being frolicking lambs or other playful small creatures. (Victor Rhythm Album Three.)

Running Game (Kirmess)

Cornelius Gurlitt, Op. 101

Free Play: Running, walking, stepping lightly, tiptoe running; clapping and tapping.
Imitative Play: Playing tag. *Play Instruments:* Clapping and tapping should prepare children for handling simple percussion instruments. The above melody suggests rhythm sticks and triangle. (Victor Rhythm Album Two.)

Skipping Is Fun

Paul Edmonds

Susan Castle

Skip-ping is fun,   skip-ping is fun,   Skip-ping is fun for ev - 'ry-one. The

long-er you skip the bet-ter you skip, So   skip-pi - ty, skip-pi - ty, skip-pi - ty, skip.

Gigue

Arcangelo Corelli

Leggiero

Free Play: Skipping, circling, whirling; galloping and trotting; clapping and tapping. *Imitative Play:* Vary skipping, etc. by drawing out from children what activity they would like to do, such as skipping to the garden to pick flowers, to the orchard to pick apples, to the field to pick pumpkins, etc. (Victor Rhythm Album One.)

13

Happy and Light · From "Bohemian Girl"

M. W. Balfe

Free Play: Skipping, tripping; hopping lightly, jumping; clapping

Imitative Play: Some children have suggested dancing like leaves, snow, or raindrops. What do your children suggest?

Play Instruments. Rhythm sticks, bells, or jingle sticks playing light tripping rhythm of melody, small drums or wood-blocks tapped on accented beats, or any instrument that your children think should be used (Victor Rhythm Album Two.)

Spanish Dance · "Preciosa"

Carl Maria von Weber

Skip

Clara Louise Anderson

Free Play: Skipping round and about; hopping lightly on both feet, clapping, tapping, etc.
Imitative Play: Hopping like frogs, rabbits, or crickets. (Victor Rhythm Album One.)

15

Round and Round We're Skipping

French Folk Tune

Round and round we're skip-ping and skip-ping, Round and round we skip - pi - ty skip,

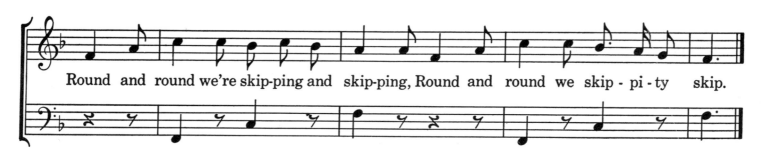

Round and round we're skip-ping and skip-ping, Round and round we skip - pi - ty skip.

Free Play: Skipping in a circle.
Imitative Play: Skipping to the orchard to pick apples; to the store to buy candy; other suggestions from children.

Sicilienne • From "Armide"

Christoph Wilibald Gluck

Free Play: Skipping; galloping; jumping; stamping; trotting; pushing and pulling; clapping.

Imitative Play: Skipping in heavy shoes or boots; stamping, pawing, and galloping like big farm horses; pedaling "bikes" up a steep hill; climbing up a high ladder, etc

Play Instruments: Skipping tune accompanied by tapping rhythm sticks; heavy accents marked by wood-blocks and drums. (Victor Rhythm Album One.)

Dance It Merrily

(Free Play: Hopping up and down; skipping and tripping; clapping.
Imitative Play: Bouncing a ball; hopping up and down like jumping jacks.)

French Folk Tune

Gently My Johnny

(Free Play: Skipping; pushing; pulling; heaving; swinging; climbing and pounding.
Imitative Play: Rowing a boat, one pull to a measure as indicated. Children will think of other things to do.)

English Folk Tune

17

We're Galloping

Children's Song

We're gal - lop - ing, gal - lop - ing all a - round,

Gal - lop - ing, gal - lop - ing round the town. Gal - lop - ing, gal - lop - ing

here we go, Gal - lop - ing, gal - lop - ing in a row.

Galloping · (Allegro · Sonata No. 13)

Franz Schubert

Free Play: Galloping. Imitative Play: Galloping like ponies. Going for a ride on a pony.

18

Here we go up, up, up,
And here we go down, down, downy,

And here we go backwards and forwards
And here we go round, round, roundy.

Nursery Rhyme

See Me Jump Up

Children's Song

See me jump up,   see me jump down,   See me jump up,   see me jump down.

Jump up, jump down, Jump up, jump down, Jump up, jump down, Jump up, jump down.

See *About Playing Instruments,* p. 137.

The Rabbit · (Les Pifferari)

Charles François Gounod

Free Play: Hopping up and down; quick leaps on tip-toes; skipping rapidly; fast gallop.

Imitative Play: Hopping like rabbits, frogs, crickets, grasshoppers, etc.; pretending to hammer, pound, or knock.

Play Instruments: Rhythm sticks, small drums, or wood-blocks on the strong beats. (Victor Rhythm Album Two.)

Tippy Tiptoe

Anonymous

Children's Song

Tip-py tip-py tip-toe here we go, Tip-py tip-py tip-toe to and fro.

Tip-py tip-py tip-toe through the house, Tip-py tip-py tip-toe like a mouse.

Tiptoe March

Italian Folk Tune

Ben marcato

Free Play: Very light, high-stepping tiptoe marching.
Imitative Play: Jack-o'-lantern parade; Halloween spooks and witches creeping about on tiptoe, trying to scare people.

Play Instruments: Tapping lightly on sticks or triangle the tiptoe notes; striking drums or wood-blocks on accented notes.

Tiptoe · (Amaryllis)

Henri Ghys

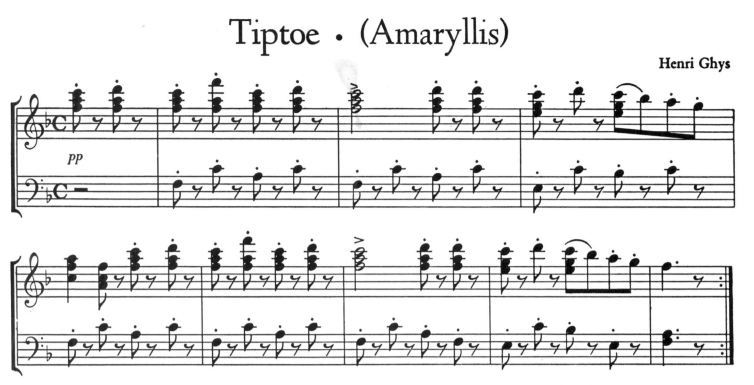

Free Play: Tiptoeing with light, dainty steps; clapping and tapping lightly.

Imitative Play: Tripping like fairies or elves; creeping like a cat after a mouse; or a cat walking in the snow.

Play Instruments: Tapping on sticks, bells, water glasses, or mixing bowls— anything that will make a clear and pleasing staccato tone or sound.

Hop Up, Hop Down

Motion Song

1. Hop up, hop down, Up and down, up and down,
2. Hands up, hands down, Up and down, up and down,
3. Heads up, heads down, Up and down, up and down,

Hop up, hop down, Hip-hip-hop-ping down.
Hands up, hands down, Hands come fall-ing down.
Heads up, heads down, Heads come nod-ding down.

See *About Playing Instruments*, p. 137.

Jumping · (Salto Mortale)

Cornelius Gurlitt, Op. 101, No. 20

Free Play: Running and jumping, climbing up (on chair or steps), then jumping down; leaping.

Imitative Play: Jumping like rabbits, crickets, grasshoppers, kittens, and puppies.

Play Instruments: The *up* and *down* of jumping can be indicated by playing on drums. If only one drum is used, have children experiment to find out whether the lighter tone is made by striking the drumhead near the center or near the rim.

(Victor Rhythm Album Two.)

Will You Come?

R.S.P.

Ruth Stephens Porter

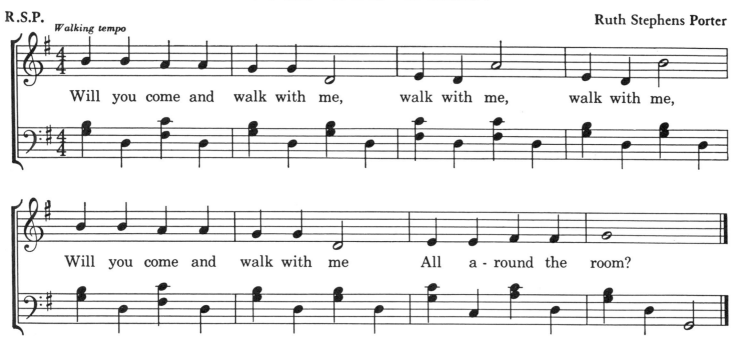

Will you come and walk with me, walk with me, walk with me,

Will you come and walk with me All a-round the room?

Let's Take a Walk · (Der kleine Wanderer)

Cornelius Gurlitt, Op. 140

Free Play: An easy, swinging walk, heads up, ready to bow to friends in passing.

Imitative Play: Walking the puppy, a doll, or a Teddy bear; going for a walk with Mother and Daddy; going to church, etc.

Walking · "The Little Traveller"

A. Gretchaninoff, Op. 98

Imitative Play: Strolling along on a sidewalk, through the park, or down a lane; walking to church. Shuffling through leaves or wading in water.

Air de Ballet

S. Jadassohn

Imitative Play: Walk in couples like elegant ladies and gentlemen. When the melody pauses at the end of the second and sixth measures, the boys may like to bow low and the girls curtsy to couples they meet. (Victor Rhythm Album Two.)

Marching to My Drum

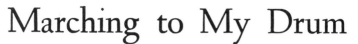

Children's Song

Tum - tum, tum-tum, tum - tum, tum - tum, Come march to the beat-ing of my

drum, drum, drum, Tum - tum, tum-tum, tum - tum, tum - tum!

MARCHES · The following suggestions for rhythmic activities may be used for all the marches in this section of this book.

Free Play: Stepping, marching, strutting, prancing; clapping, tapping.

Imitative Play: Playing soldier—marching past the flag ·and saluting it; being a marching band or circus parade with all the trappings that children think up; buglers (when there are bugle calls in the music), drum majors, flag-bearers, etc.

Play Instruments: Children will like to make the toy bugle calls with cupped hands. Drums could be both real and imaginary for keeping the steady march step.

Phrasing: Phrase ending could be indicated by changing direction of marching, prancing, etc.; phrase endings could be marked by hand claps or a cymbal crash.

March

Cornelius Gurlitt, Op. 140

Vivace, ma non troppo

Victor Rhythm Album Two.

25

Tramp, Tramp

Anonymous

Paul Forde

Tramp, tramp, tramp-ing, tramp-ing, Stamp, stamp, stamp-ing, stamp-ing,

Up the high road, down the low, Tramp-ing, stamp-ing, here we go.

Military March

Clara Louise Anderson

Trumpet call

Marching

Victor Rhythm Album One.

26

In a Line

Arranged from a French Tune

In a line we go, In a line, in a line, In a

line we go, In a line we go.

March

Finnish

27

The Tin Soldiers Marching

A. Gretchaninoff, Op. 98, No. 3

Imitative Play: Marching with the stiff, jerky movements of tin or wooden soldiers.

Soldiers' March · From "Faust"

Charles François Gounod

Roll

(*Rolling Balls:* Large, soft balls are easiest for children to handle. Two children sit on the floor facing each other and roll the ball back and forth.)

Louella Garrett

Roll, . . here it comes, you see, Roll, . . roll it back to me.

Roll, Roll the Ball

Game Song

Roll, roll the ball, . . Roll, roll to me. . .

Roll, roll the ball, . . Roll back to me. . .

Harvest Home

Henry Purcell

With an easy swing

29

See-Saw

From "365 Bedtime Nursery Rhymes"

Susan Castle

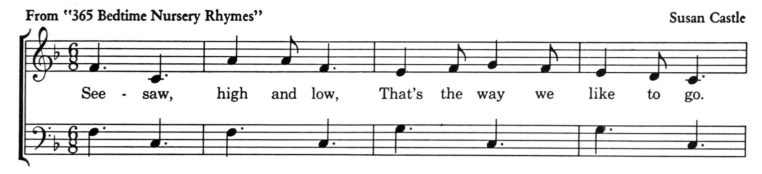

See - saw, high and low, That's the way we like to go.

With a bound up we fly From the ground to the sky.

See-Saw, Sacradown

Old Rhyme

See - saw, sac - ra - down, This is the way to Lon - don Town.

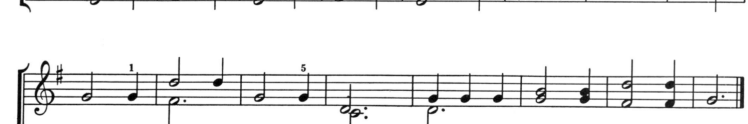

First go up and then go down, That is the way to Lon - don Town.

Imitative Play: 1. Children enjoy "seesawing" with arms stretched sideways, moving "up down, up down" on accented beats.

2. Hands on hips, two children face: first child stretching up on "see" (*up*), second child squatting on heels on "saw" (*down*), continuing to alternate the *up* and *down* on strong accents (first beat in each measure).

3. Two children seated facing, hands clasped, seesawing back and forth with push-pull on accented beats.

Swinging

Children's Song

Swing - ing, I'm swing - ing, See me swing up high.

Swing - ing, I'm swing - ing, See me touch the sky.

Imitative Play: 1. Children (seated) use hands to push the swing out with vigorous motion: hands *out* on first measure, *back* on second, etc.

2. Children (standing), right foot side-front, hands holding the swing rope, whole body swings forward on first measure, back on next, and so on.

Waltz

Johannes Brahms, Op. 39, No. 2

Free Play: Swinging, swaying, and rocking.

Imitative Play: Swinging in a swing; skating on the ice, or roller skating to school; rowing a boat; tossing balloons into the air, or waving them back and forth on a string; imagining they are trees and flowers waving in the breeze. (Victor Rhythm Album Two.)

I'll Skate on My Roller Skates

S.C.

Susan Castle

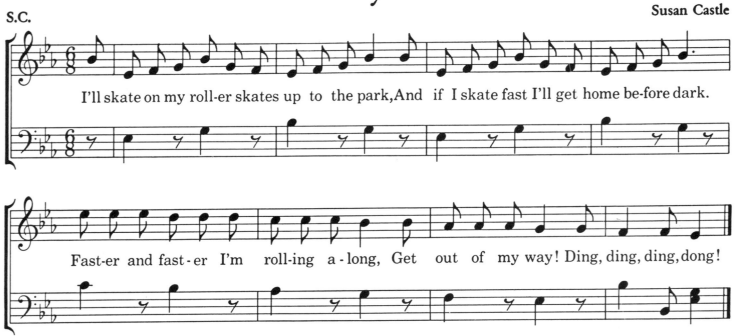

I'll skate on my roll-er skates up to the park, And if I skate fast I'll get home be-fore dark.

Fast-er and fast-er I'm roll-ing a-long, Get out of my way! Ding, ding, ding, dong!

Roller Skating • (The Reaper's Song)

Robert Schumann, Op. 68, No. 18

Imitative Play: (*Seated*) Children make skating motions with arms.
(*Standing*) Children go through the motions of skating.

About Eating and Resting

A child's distinction between work and play is slight. In school, children enjoy taking responsibility for helping set the table, tending plants, arranging books and playthings, and feeding pets.

From time immemorial all people have made songs as they worked. Children are no exception. They will sing to a rabbit or a canary bird, the fish in a bowl of water, or the bread and milk that they are to eat.

Choose from the field of folk music some songs that are familiar and simple in structure. Using these melodies, encourage the children to "make up" words about whatever they are interested in at the moment. See page xvii

Polly, Put the Kettle On

Mother Goose

German

Polly, put the ket - tle on, Pol - ly, put the ket - tle on,

Pol - ly, put the ket - tle on, We'll all have tea.

Suggested extra verse: Susie, set the table now, Susie, set the table now. Tommy, put the cookies on, And I'll get the milk.

Free Play: An excellent rhythm for clapping and tapping very quickly and lightly with hands and fingers. To vary, tap on glasses, bells, tables, or rhythm sticks. The music "runs" too. (Victor Rhythm Album Three.)

Drink Your Milk

Adapted

French Folk Tune

Drink your milk, Bet-ty, drink your milk, Bet-ty, Drink it like a la - dy.

Drink your milk, Bet-ty, drink your milk, Bet-ty, Drink your milk like a la - dy.

33

After work and play comes a time for rest. Music can be very helpful in creating the right mood for rest. Many children hum or sing a familiar song to themselves as they relax. Others sing-talk themselves into either sleep or relaxation. Selections inducing calmness and quiet may be played on the piano or phonograph.

It often happens, when excitement has run high in a group, that tension can be loosened best through rhythmic response.

Whenever possible have children sprawl on floor mats, then roll over, stretch, hump up their backs, crawl, and so on, to music.

This Is My Sleepy Time

Grace Haynes

James Barton

This is my sleep-y time, My hands and feet are still. . . My head is down, my eyes are closed, This is my sleep-y time. .

Waltz

Franz Schubert, Op. 33, No. 7

Victor Rhythm Album Four.

Dance of the Happy Spirits · From "Orpheus"

Christoph Wilibald Gluck

Resting Time • (Ernste Stunde)

Cornelius Gurlitt, Op. 140

Now It's Time to Rest

L.G.

Louella Garrett

Now it's time to rest, Like rob-ins in the nest. Tuck their heads be-

neath their wing, Close their eyes to ev-'ry-thing. Now we rest, Now we rest.

About Counting

Counting songs are favorites with children. With the "ten fingers and ten toes and but one mouth and one nose," they begin with themselves to rhyme, sing, dance, and play games with counting chants. "A Song About Me," p. 3, and the "finger and toe" songs on pages 50, 51, may also be used as counting songs.

One, two, three,
What can this be?
Every child is counting
One, two, three.

One, two, three,
What's in the tree?
Four little birds
Looking at me.

One, Two, Buckle My Shoe

Mother Goose

Traditional

One, two, buck-le my shoe. Three, four, o-pen the door.

Five, six, pick up some sticks. Sev'n, eight, lay them straight.

Two Little Birds

Traditional

Two lit-tle birds sat on a hill. One named Jack and the oth-er named Jill.
(Thumbs are the birds)   *Right thumb up.*   *Left thumb up.*

Fly a-way Jack, fly a-way Jill! Come back Jack, come back Jill!
Right thumb flies over shoulder.   *Left thumb flies over shoulder.*   *Right thumb returns.*   *Left thumb returns.*

Here Is the Beehive

From "The Rooster Crows"

Traditional

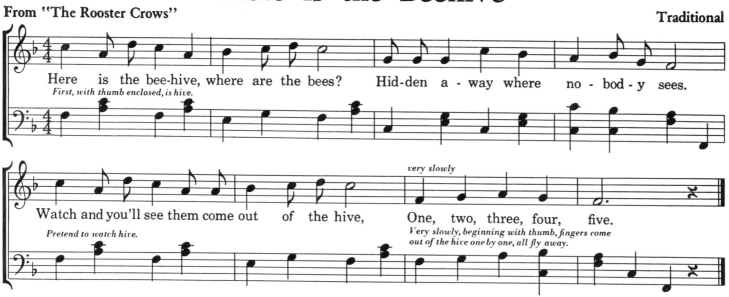

Here is the bee-hive, where are the bees? Hid-den a-way where no-bod-y sees.

First, with thumb enclosed, is hive.

Watch and you'll see them come out of the hive, One, two, three, four, five.

Pretend to watch hive.

very slowly

Very slowly, beginning with thumb, fingers come out of the hive one by one, all fly away.

At the close of the song children will enjoy imitating the flight
of the five bees by buzzing and waving their hands in the air.

Five Little Chickadees

Singing Game

1. Five lit-tle chick-a-dees, Peep-ing at the door, One flew a-way And
2. Four lit-tle chick-a-dees, Sit-ting in a tree, One flew a-way And
3. Three lit-tle chick-a-dees, Look-ing at you, One flew a-way And

then there were four.
then there were three.   Chick-a-dee, chick-a-dee,
then there were two.

CHORUS

Hap-py and gay, Chick-a-dee, chick-a-dee, Fly a-way.

4. Two little chickadees,
   Sitting in the sun,
   One flew away
   And then there was one.

5. One little chickadee,
   Left all alone,
   It flew away
   And then there was none.

37

About Playing Games

Ring-a-ring of little boys,
Ring-a-ring of girls,
All around, all around
Twists and twirls.

Kate Greenaway

Dancing in a ring or circle is one of the first forms of co-operation in the play activities of children. The singing games that follow are examples which are universally popular with children. This is because they originated in an innate desire to belong to, to play with, and to be accepted by one's playmates.

Ring-Around a Rosy

Children's Game

Ring - a - round a ros - y, Pock - et full of pos - y,
Hands joined, move left in circle.

Push, push, push, push, And all fall down.
Stop! Push hands up, up, up. Fall down.

Dancing in a Ring · "Tarantella"

Stephen Heller, Op. 85, No. 2

Presto

Victor Rhythm Album Three.

38

Round and Round a Circle · "Ringel, Ringel, Reihe"

Translated by Mary E. Holland

German Singing Game

Round and round a cir - cle Go the hap - py chil - dren,

Hands joined, circle around a child who is the bird.

Go up to the li - lac bush, Bird - ie flies a - way, hush, hush.

Circle moves toward the center.   *Bird tries to fly out of the circle.*

Sally Go Round the Stars

English Singing Game

Sal - ly go round the stars, Sal - ly go round the moon.

Sal - ly go round the chim - ney pots On a Sun - day aft - er - noon. *Whoops!*

Children make a circle with hands joined and slide to the left as they sing.
They drop each other's hands and, with hands raised over heads, jump in air
and clap hands when they sing "Whoops!"

Round and Round the Village

English Singing Game

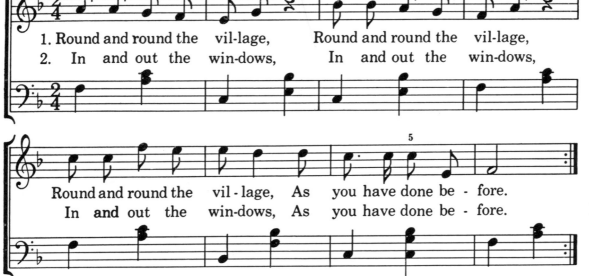

1. Round and round the vil-lage, Round and round the vil-lage,
2. In and out the win-dows, In and out the win-dows,

Round and round the vil-lage, As you have done be-fore.
In and out the win-dows, As you have done be-fore.

1st stanza: Children stand in a ring with hands joined. One child (leader) walks or skips around out-side the ring.

2d stanza: Children raise joined hands as leader goes in and out under arches.

3. Stand and face your partner,
Stand and face your partner,
Stand and face your partner,
As you have done before.

3d stanza: Leader stops inside ring and faces his choice for partner.

4. Follow her to London,
Follow her to London,
Follow her to London,
As you have done before.

4th stanza: Leader runs out of ring pursued by partner. Group re-peats this stanza until child is caught.

Repeat game with "partner" becoming the "leader."

Cat and Mouse

Translated

Puerto Rico

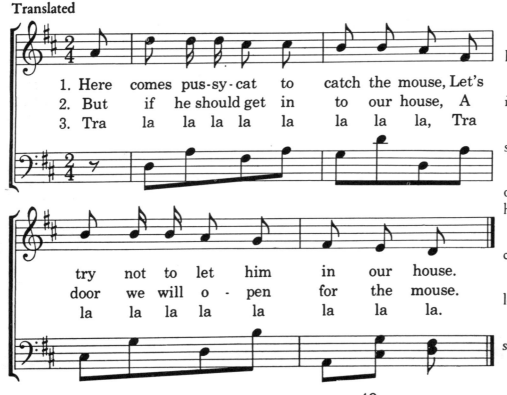

1. Here comes pus-sy-cat to catch the mouse, Let's
2. But if he should get in to our house, A
3. Tra la la la la la la la la, Tra

try not to let him in our house.
door we will o-pen for the mouse.
la la la la la la la la.

Game: Children form a circle with hands joined.

The "cat" is outside, the mouse inside the circle.

Group sings the first two stanzas, standing still and holding hands high.

"Cat" walks around the circle, and only when he tries to get in may hands be lowered.

When "cat" finally breaks in, cir-cle permits mouse to run out.

If "cat" is clever enough, he fol-lows mouse and catches her.

Group repeats the "Tra la la" stanza until the mouse is caught.

Squirrels and Trees

Children's Game

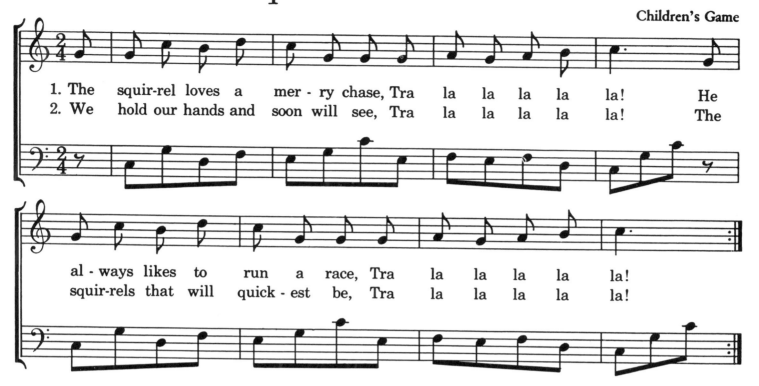

1. The squir-rel loves a mer-ry chase, Tra la la la la la! He
2. We hold our hands and soon will see, Tra la la la la la! The

al-ways likes to run a race, Tra la la la la la!
squir-rels that will quick-est be, Tra la la la la la!

Children in couples, forming a circle, are trees. Each couple joins hands to make a hollow in the tree. In each hollow tree stands a squirrel. Inside the circle of trees are three extra "squirrels." When song begins, *all* squirrels run and chase each other inside circle. On singing final "Tra la la la la la!" each of the squirrels looks for a hollow tree to hide in. The three left over are extra squirrels, who return to the center as the game begins again.

Frog in the Middle

Children's Game

Frog in the mid-dle and he can't get out, He can't get out, he can't get out.

Frog in the mid-dle and he can't get out, Take a stick and poke him out.

A child squatting and jumping about in center of circle is the frog. Group with hands joined circle around the "frog," singing "Frog in the middle," etc. until they sing "Take a stick." Then circle stops and moves toward "frog," pretending to "poke" at him with imaginary sticks. "Frog" has to escape by jumping outside the closing-in circle of children. New "frog" is chosen and game is repeated.

A-Hunting We Will Go

English

Oh! a - hunt - ing we will go, A - hunt - ing we will go, We'll

catch a fox and put him in a box, And then we'll let him go.

Children in couples, hand in hand, are hunters. They gallop after fox.
Couple catching fox join both hands to box him in.

Hunting Song

Robert Schumann

Free Play: Galloping, running, stamping feet.
Imitative Play: Going hunting on a horse—galloping away, loosening and
tightening reins, spurring the horse on, slowing up, stamping in impatience, etc.
Play Instruments: Wood-blocks, or the halves of coconut shells clapped
together, make fine sound effects for hoofbeats   (Victor Rhythm Album One.)

The Farmer in the Dell

Singing Game

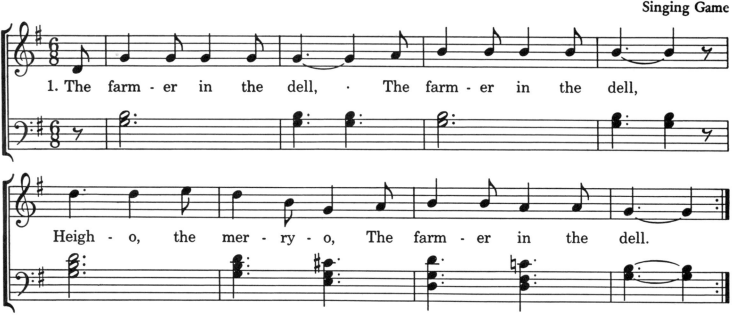

1. The farm-er in the dell, · The farm-er in the dell,

Heigh - o, the mer - ry - o, The farm - er in the dell.

2. The farmer takes a wife, etc.
3. The wife takes the child, etc.
4. The child takes the nurse, etc.

5. The nurse takes the dog, etc.
6. The dog takes the cat, etc.

7. The cat takes the rat, etc.
8. The rat takes the cheese, etc.
9. The cheese stands alone, etc.

Group forms large circle, which moves and sings continuously up to final verse.

1. Farmer stands in center.
2. Farmer takes from circle a wife.
3. Wife takes from circle a child.

4. Child takes from circle a nurse.
5. Nurse takes from circle a dog.
6. Dog takes from circle a cat.

7. Cat takes from circle a rat.
8. Rat takes from circle the cheese.
9. Group stops, claps hands.

Child who "stands alone" remains in circle to become "farmer" when game is repeated.

Guessing Game

Children's Game

Not too fast

[1]   [2]

We're ver - y, ver - y tall, Now we are ver - y small.

[3]   [4]   [5]

Some - times tall, some - times small, Guess what we are now?

Children stand in circle facing center. The child who is "it" stands in middle with eyes closed. One child in the circle is chosen leader. At [1] children stand on tiptoes, [2] children squat, [3] and [4] children move up and down, [5] leader indicates whether the group will be tall or small. If "it" guesses right, the circle will clap.

About Home Folks

When mother comes each morning
She wears her oldest things,
She doesn't make a rustle,
She hasn't any rings;

She says, "Good morning, chickies,
It's such a lovely day,
Let's go into the garden
And have a game of play."

Rose Fyleman

The happiest and most lasting bonds that can be made between school and home are those created by mutually valued interchanges.

Not every home sends songs to the school, but most homes send willing learners. The school can reciprocate by giving children songs that they, in turn, can take home and sing to "my daddy," "my mamma," or "my baby."

Whether songs about home and family life are learned at school, at home, or from playing with older children is not the important point. The spirit of the songs and games

that young children sing and play with older people is what counts. And the spirit is right when a game song for the baby embodies an affectionate interest in a small learner, to whom everything, including his own fingers and toes, is brand-new.

This is the reason why simple action songs continue to delight generation after generation of children. "This Little Pig," "Knock at the Door," and "Ride a Cock Horse" have their equivalents in the children's songs of every race of people on earth.

Get Up!

Children's Song

Good Morning

Marian Major

Hiding

Dorothy Aldis

L.B.P

1. I'm hid-ing, I'm hid-ing and no one knows where; For
2. "We've hunt-ed," sighed Moth-er, "as hard as we could For

all they can see is my toes and my hair.
I'm so a-fraid we have lost him for good."

Up, down! Up, down!
All the way to London town—
See how fast we're going!
Feel the jar
Of the car?
Feel the wind a-blowing?

Up, down! Up, down!
All the way to London town—
Here we are this minute!
Rock the chair
Anywhere
When we two are in it.

Rock, Rock, Rock

P.F.

Paul Forde

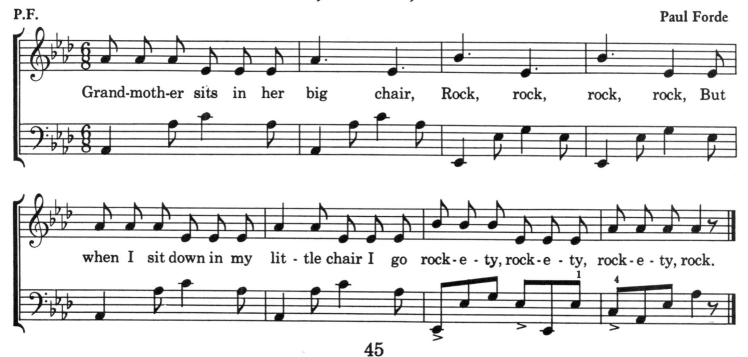

Grand-moth-er sits in her big chair, Rock, rock, rock, rock, But

when I sit down in my lit-tle chair I go rock-e-ty, rock-e-ty, rock-e-ty, rock.

45

Walking

Grace Glaubitz

James Barton

When Dad-dy walks with Jean and me, We have a lot of fun 'Cause
we can't walk as fast as he, Un - less we skip and run and run and
run and run and run, Un - less we skip and run and run and run.

Imitative Play: Play "Air de Ballet," by Jadassohn (Victor Rhythm Album Two), on the phonograph. First time the melody is played it sounds like the brisk steps of Daddy's walk. When it is repeated the quick, light step-ping of "Jean and me" is heard. The boys could be "Daddy," following the steady walking rhythm; the girls, "Jean and me" as they follow the tripping figures of the music.

I Have a Little Sister

Kansas City School Children

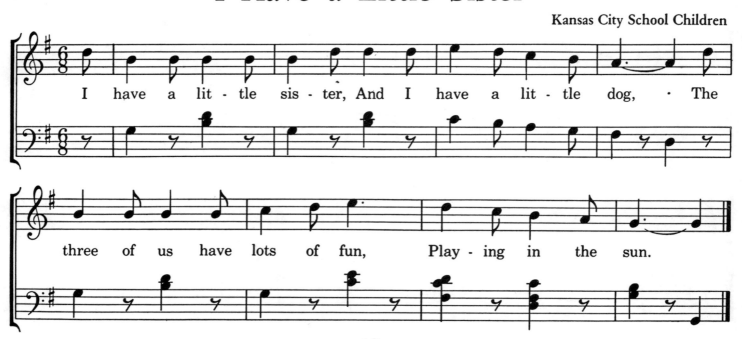

I have a lit - tle sis - ter, And I have a lit - tle dog, The
three of us have lots of fun, Play - ing in the sun.

Our Baby

I am a little thing;
I am not very high;
I laugh, dance and sing,
And sometimes I cry.

I have ten fingers too,
And just as many toes;
Two eyes to see through,
And but one little nose.

Eliza Lee Follen

Pinky Winky Baby

I.C.K.

Ida C. Knapp

My pink-y wink-y ba-by Has pink-y wink-y toes; And pink-y wink-y dim-ples, And a round lit-tle nose. Pink-y wink-y ba-by, Pink-y wink-y woo, Pink-y wink-y ba-by I love you.

What Are Babies Made Of?

Traditional

Oh, what are ba-bies made of, made of, Oh, what are ba-bies made of? Plums and crumbs and toes and thumbs, And that's what ba-bies are made of.

47

Dance a Baby Diddy

Traditional

Dance a ba - by did - dy, Who'll find chick - a - bid - dy?

Look in the barn, do her no harm, And dance a ba - by did - dy.

Dancing Song

Translated

Carl Reinecke

Ding dong, come a - long, Here's our ba - by danc - ing.

Ding dong, come a - long, Here's our ba - by danc - ing.

Imitative Play: With both of these songs children pretend to bounce a baby,
a doll, or a pet on their knees.

Pat-a-Cake

Mother Goose

Pat-a-cake, pat-a-cake, bak - er's man, Bake me a cake as fast as you can.

Pat it and prick it and mark it with B, To put in the ov - en for Ba - by and me.

Clapping Game

Russian

Not too fast

Clap - ping, clap - ping, soft - ly clap. Clap - ping, clap - ping, clap, clap, clap.

Roll them o - ver, o - ver so, Now get read - y, off we go.

Clap - ping, clap - ping, soft - ly clap, Clap - ping, clap - ping, clap, clap, clap.

Play Instruments: The clapping rhythm of these songs may be carried over into playing accompaniments with rhythm and jingle sticks.

49

Knock at the Door

Traditional

Knock at the door, peep in, Lift the latch and walk in.

Knock on forehead.   *Lift eyelids with fingers.*   *Pull nose.*   *Put finger in open mouth.*

This Little Pig

Old Rhyme

Henry M. Halvorson

This lit-tle pig went to mar-ket, This lit-tle pig stayed at home,

This lit-tle pig had roast beef, This lit-tle pig had none, And

this lit-tle pig cried, "Wee, wee, wee!" All the way home.

May be played with fingers or toes as "piggies."

Finger Song

Translated

Norwegian

Thumb-man, Lick-pan, Tall-man, Ring-man, Lit-tle, lit-tle Play-man.

Pitter and Patter are—what do you s'pose?
Two little feet with ten little toes
That belong to a dear little boy I know.
They take him wherever he wants to go.

Where Is Thumbkin?

Finger Game

French

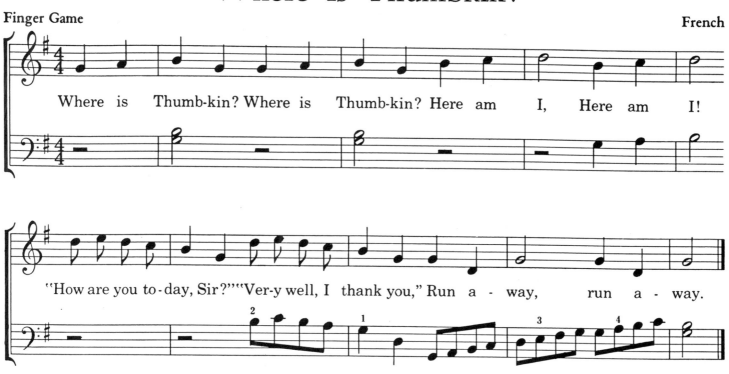

Where is Thumb-kin? Where is Thumb-kin? Here am I, Here am I!

"How are you to-day, Sir?" "Ver-y well, I thank you," Run a - way, run a - way.

Finger Game

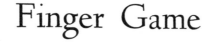

Traditional

Thumb-kin says, "I'll dance," Thumb-kin says, "I'll sing."

Dance and sing you mer-ry lit-tle men, Thumb-kin says, "I'll dance and sing."

2. Pointer says, "I'll dance," etc.   4. Ring man says, "I'll dance," etc.
3. Tall man says, "I'll dance," etc.   5. Little man says, "I'll dance," etc.

51

Foot-Riding Songs

This group of songs may be used by school children, pretending to ride a baby, a dolly, or a kitty, as on Daddy's foot.

For playing pony and horse, each child gallops around the room and finally back "to the stable." Riding a stick horse adds to the fun.

The instrumental numbers are particularly appropriate for galloping, which is an easy rhythm for young children, since its pattern does not require alternating between right foot and left foot.

Ride a Cock Horse

Old Rhyme

Traditional

1. Ride a cock horse to Ban - bur - y Cross To see a fine la - dy up-
2. Ride a cock horse to Ban - bur - y Cross To buy my big Tom - my a

on a white horse, With rings on her fin - gers and
gal - lop - ing horse, To trot - trot and gal - lop and

bells on her toes, She shall have mu - sic wher - ev - er she goes.
prance up and down, He shall go rid - ing all o - ver the town.

Galloping Horses

Clara Louise Anderson

Free Play: Galloping, bouncing up and down, loping, leaping, hopping.

Imitative Play: Pretending to be a pony, or to be riding on a horse or a donkey. Pretending Daddy to ride a baby or a doll or a pet on a foot or knee.

(Victor Rhythm Album One.)

52

Ride-a, Ride-a Pony

Translated

Norwegian Folk Song

Ride - a, ride - a po - ny,

Po - ny's name is Dad - dy, Dad - dy's foot goes up and down,

Lit - tle Bob - by he stays on, Oh, ride - a, ride - a po - ny.

Presto · Op. 31, No. 3

Ludwig van Beethoven

Presto con fuoco

Free Play: Galloping, bouncing up and down, loping, leaping, hopping.
Imitative Play: Pretending to be a pony or riding on a horse or a donkey.
Riding a baby, a doll, or a pet on a foot or knee.

53

To Market, to Market

Old Rhyme

Traditional

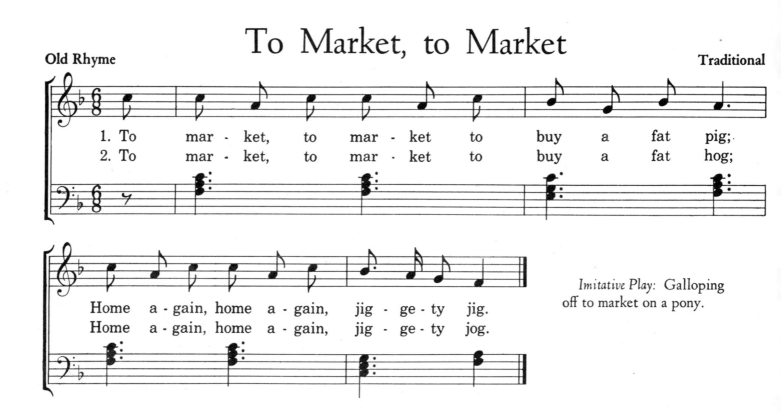

1. To mar - ket, to mar - ket to buy a fat pig;
2. To mar - ket, to mar - ket to buy a fat hog;

Home a - gain, home a - gain, jig - ge - ty jig.
Home a - gain, home a - gain, jig - ge - ty jog.

Imitative Play: Galloping off to market on a pony.

The Knight of the Hobby Horse

Robert Schumann, simplified

Free Play: Rocking, swaying, rolling body from side to side.

Imitative Play: Riding on a rocking horse. (Children stand, right foot out, both hands extended to hold reins. Swing weight of body forward on right foot, back on left, in time to music.) (Victor Rhythm Album Three.)

Going to Bed

Bed Time

G.H.   Graham Haswell

One, two, three, four, five, six, sev'n, eight, Hur-ry to bed; it's get-ting late.

One, two, three, four, five, six, sev'n, eight, Bet-ter hur-ry up; it's get-ting late.

Hippity Hop to Bed

Leroy Jackson[1]   Susan Castle

Gaily

Oh, it's hip-pi-ty hop to bed, · · I'd rath-er sit up in-stead, But when

Fath-er says "must" There's noth-ing but just Go hip-pi-ty hop to bed.

[1]Courtesy of the *Woman's Home Companion*, copyright The Crowell-Collier Publishing Company, and the author.

My Dream

B.N.

Bobby Nickson

I ride my po-ny a-way to bed, A cow-boy big am I. My

gun and hol-ster, they are red, I say, "Ki-yip-py-yi!"

Gid-dap!

P.F.

Paul Forde

Gid-dap, gid-dap, gid-dap, gid-dap, We're rid-ing our po-nies to bed, gid-dap!

ritard

WHOA! WHOA! WHOA! WHOA! This is as far as we go.

Riding a Stick-Horse

A. Gretchaninoff, Op. 98, No. 5

Getting pretty tired.

Galloping home, tired but happy.

Listening; or Dramatic Play: The music tells the story.
Encourage the children to give their own interpretation of it.

Lullaby, oh, lullaby!
Flowers are closed and lambs are sleeping;
Lullaby, oh, lullaby!
Stars are up; the moon is peeping;
Lullaby, oh, lullaby!
Sleep, my baby, fall a-sleeping,
Lullaby, oh, lullaby.

Christina G. Rossetti

To Baby Land

Old Lullaby

How man-y miles to Ba - by Land? An - y-one can tell;
What do they do in Ba - by Land? Dream and wake and play;

Up one flight, to the right, Please to ring the bell.
Laugh and crow, fond - er grow, Jol - ly times have they.

Bye, Baby Bunting

Mother Goose

Old Lullaby

Bye, Ba - by Bunt - ing, Dad - dy's gone a - hunt - ing, To

catch a lit - tle rab - bit skin, To wrap his Ba - by Bunt - ing in.

Sleep, Baby, Sleep

German Cradle Song

Sleep, ba-by, sleep! Thy fa-ther guards the sheep, Thy moth-er shakes the dream-land tree, And

from it falls sweet dreams for thee; Sleep, ba - by, sleep! Sleep, ba-by, sleep.

Cradle Song · Op. 12, No. 6

Robert Schumann

Moderato semplice

For quiet listening.

59

Don't Drop Your Shoes

Children's Song

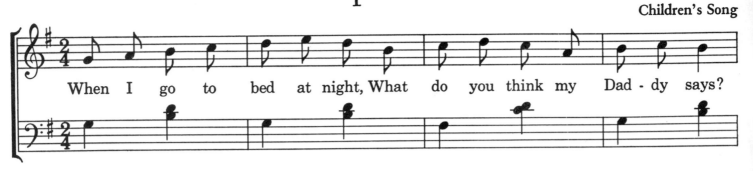

When I go to bed at night, What do you think my Dad-dy says?

"Don't drop your shoes on the floor!"

I Always Want My Teddy Bear

Audrey F. Carpenter   Paul Forde

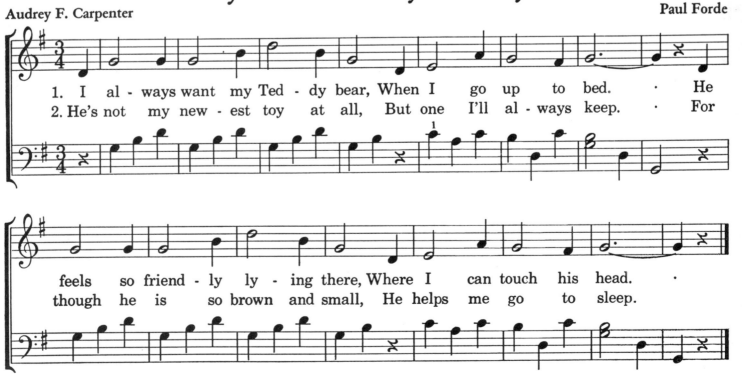

1. I al-ways want my Ted-dy bear, When I go up to bed. · He
2. He's not my new-est toy at all, But one I'll al-ways keep. · For

feels so friend-ly ly-ing there, Where I can touch his head. ·
though he is so brown and small, He helps me go to sleep.

Sleep, My Birdies

French Folk Tune

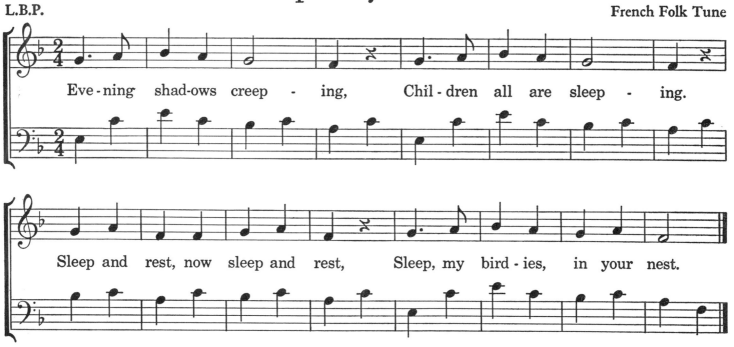

Eve-ning shad-ows creep - ing, Chil-dren all are sleep - ing.

Sleep and rest, now sleep and rest, Sleep, my bird-ies, in your nest.

Lullaby · Op. 13, No. 7

Alexander Iljinsky

Poco andante

Free Play: Rocking; swinging; swaying.
Imitative Play: Rock the baby's cradle or carriage. Pretend to be swaying trees rocking baby birds in their nests; flowers nodding their go-to-sleep songs.
Mood: Quiet and peaceful. Music to be listened to for its beautiful melody.
(Victor Rhythm Album Three.)

About My Prayers

My Prayer

Mary Mapes Dodge

When I run a-bout and play, When I kneel at night to pray, God bless me, God bless me.

Prayer

Elizabeth McE. Shields

John Langland

You put the sun to rest each night And light the sun and moon; I'm

glad, dear God, for I'm a child Who goes to bed quite soon.

We Thank Thee, Dear Lord

L.B.P.

Alfred Paulson

For love and for good - ness, We thank Thee, dear Lord. For

keep - ing us safe from harm, We thank Thee, dear Lord.

About Folks We Like to Know

All the butchers and the bakers,
All the cake and candy makers,

Come the gorgeous blue police,

Comes a tailor spic and span
And a scissors-grinder man.

Mildred Meigs

Children are born imitators, it is said, and it is true, for imitation is one of the first and most important steps in learning. Through imitating what they see and hear they store up an accumulation of feelings, images, and ideas which, when assimilated, are used for both reflection and communication

Children learn what other people mean to them, not through instruction and knowledge, but by feeling. And the child's power to *feel* out *for* and *into* the essential *quality* that is a person or a thing is what he uses to create the kind of images of people and things that helps him to interpret future needs as they arise.

Action intensifies imagery and makes it meaningful. A small boy not only *imitates* what he observes about a policeman, an airplane, or an elephant, but he *is* any one of the three at will. *Being* a milkman, or the milkman's horse, by acting out a part is a child's way of affirming his impressions to the point of making them consciously useful images. Without them, the arbitrary symbols used in both language and music are bound to be meaningless.

Both imitative and dramatic play associated with song and dance help children to increase their store of musical meanings. Children should be encouraged to make up songs of their own about "folk we like to know."

The Postman

Kansas City School Children

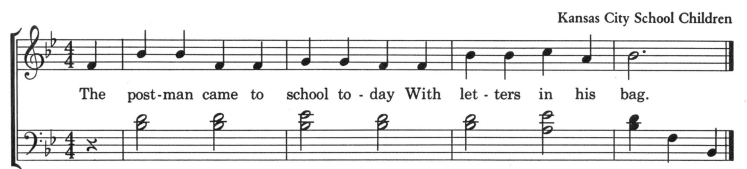

The post-man came to school to-day With let-ters in his bag.

The Popcorn Man

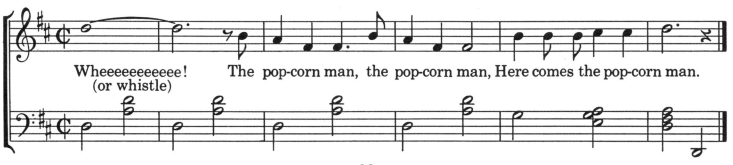

Wheeeeeeeeeee! (or whistle) The pop-corn man, the pop-corn man, Here comes the pop-corn man.

63

I'm the police cop man, I am, I am.
Cars can't go till I say they can.

Margaret Morrison

I'm a Traffic Cop

I am a traf-fic cop, I tell the cars to go, I tell the cars to STOP!

The Policeman

Children's Song

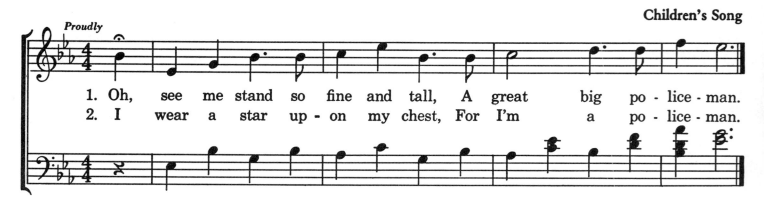

1. Oh, see me stand so fine and tall, A great big po-lice-man.
2. I wear a star up-on my chest, For I'm a po-lice-man.

The Milk Man's Horse

Mississippi Children's Game Song

1. Gid-dap, gid-dap, gid-dap, lit-tle horse, Now stop and wait, The
2. Gid-dap, gid-dap, gid-dap, lit-tle horse, Now stop and wait, Here's

milk I'll leave right at the front door, So stand by the gate.
milk to leave for the chil-dren next door, So stand there and wait.

The barber snips and snips
My hair with his scissors,
And then he zips on.

It clips
Up and down
And around
My hair in back.

Ssss ssss
It swishes
On the sides
Behind my ears.

Ssss ssss
It tickles
As it slides
Straight up the middle
Of my neck.

Dorothy Baruch

Barber Song

M.E.N.

Marion Esther Nichols

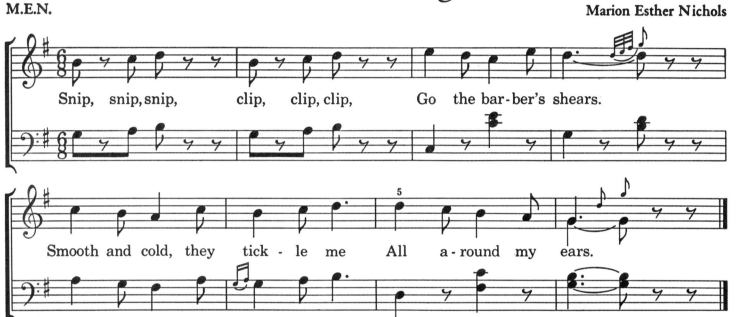

Snip, snip, snip, clip, clip, clip, Go the bar-ber's shears.

Smooth and cold, they tick-le me All a-round my ears.

The Firemen

Oo - oo - oo - oo - oo - oo - oo - oo, Cling, clang, cling, clang, cling, clang. Get

out of our way, get out of our way! That's what the fire-bells say.

The Coal Man's coming at half-past nine.
The Coal Man's rather a friend of mine.

His face and his hands and clothes are black,
And coal dust covers each bulging sack.

In every sack is a hundredweight,
And the Coal Man's name is Mr. Tait.

And that's just one of the things I know,
'Cos Kate, the Housemaid, told me so.

And though he's old and terribly strong,
And he's coaling, coaling all day long,

And Kate says Mr. Tait is white
When he washes his hands and face at night,

But, Mr. Coal Man Tait, you're far,
Far nicer, grimy as you are.

Hugh Chesterman

The Coal Man

S.C.

Susan Castle

I'm the Organ-Grinder Man

J.S.

Jack Sutton

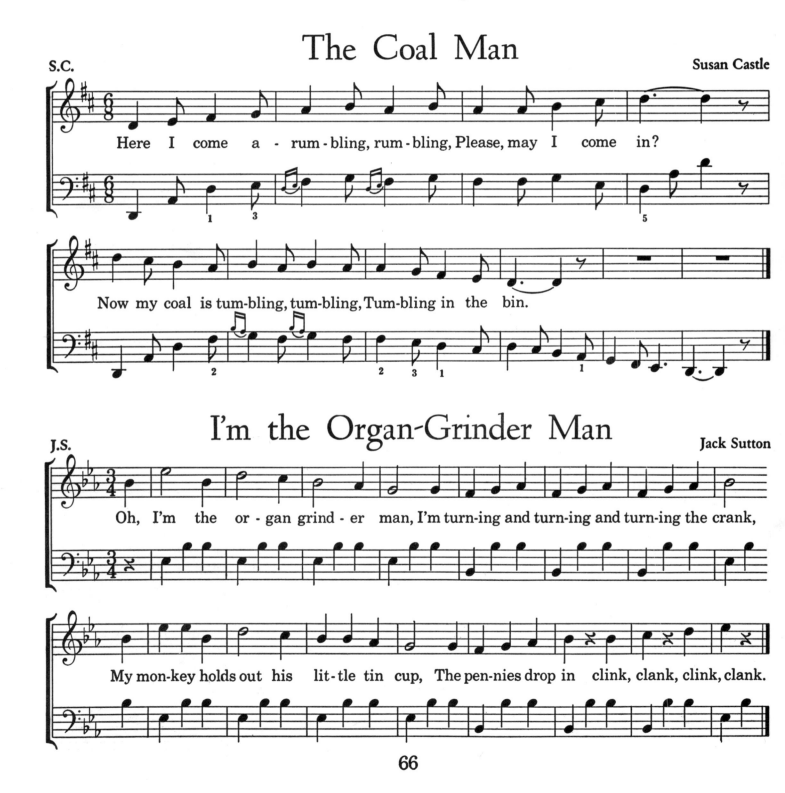

Here I come a - rum - bling, rum - bling, Please, may I come in?

Now my coal is tum - bling, tum - bling, Tum - bling in the bin.

Oh, I'm the or - gan grind - er man, I'm turn - ing and turn - ing and turn - ing the crank,

My mon - key holds out his lit - tle tin cup, The pen - nies drop in clink, clank, clink, clank.

About Songland Folks

No music book for children would be complete without some of these old and loved friends from songland.

Here are familiar songs that children enjoy for their word sounds alone. They are more fun when jingly tunes and lively rhythms keep pace with rhyming words.

The stories they tell stimulate the imagination and appeal to the love of the dramatic that is in every child.

Nothing is more satisfying to a small child than to play the part that is, to him, the most important role in a song story.

The majority of the songs in this section center about one leading character. An entire group of children can have the fun of impersonating, each in his own way, Little Jack Horner, Handy Spandy, and others.

"Little Bo-Peep" and "Hey, Diddle, Diddle" are exceptions, and, in both instances, each boy or girl is likely to want to be the entire cast. There is nothing incongruous to a child in being Little Bo-Peep one minute and a lost sheep the next; nor in moving in rapid succession from the part of a fiddling cat to that of a cow jumping over the moon, nor from a laughing dog to a dish running away with a spoon.

Preparatory to, and parallel with, the more highly organized forms of dramatic expression, children need much experience in being "the whole show." Songs that have the simple directness of these well-known folk rhymes are ideal for the "let me" and being "it" phase of child growth.

Little Boy Blue

Mother Goose   Traditional

Lit-tle Boy Blue, come blow your horn, The sheep's in the mead-ow, the cow's in the corn; Where is the boy who looks aft-er the sheep? He's un-der the 'hay-stack fast a-sleep.

Little Jack Horner

Mother Goose

J. W. Elliott

Lit-tle Jack Horn-er Sat in a corn-er, Eat-ing a Christ-mas pie; He

put in his thumb, And pulled out a plum, And said, "What a good boy am I!"

Humpty Dumpty

Mother Goose

Traditional

Hump-ty Dump-ty sat on a wall, Hump-ty Dump-ty

had a great fall. All the king's hors-es and all the king's men,

Could-n't put Hump-ty to-geth-er a-gain.

Little Bo-Peep

Mother Goose

J. W. Elliott

Lit-tle Bo-peep has lost her sheep, And can't tell where to find them;

Leave them a-lone, and they'll come home, Wag-ging their tails be-hind them.

Hey, Diddle, Diddle

Mother Goose

J. W. Elliott

Hey, did-dle, did-dle, the cat and the fid-dle, The

cow jumped o-ver the moon, The lit-tle dog laughed to

see such sport And the dish ran a-way with the spoon.

Handy Spandy

Old Rhyme

Traditional

Han - dy Span - dy, Jack - a - dan - dy, Loved plum-cake and sug - ar can-dy. He bought some at the gro-cer's shop, And out he came a - hop - hop - hop.

Little Polly Flinders

Mother Goose

English Folk Tune

Lit - tle Pol - ly Flin - ders Sat a - mong the cin - ders, Warm - ing her pret - ty lit - tle toes. Her moth - er came and caught her, And spanked her lit - tle daugh - ter, For spoil - ing her nice new clothes.

About Happy Holidays

No festival is complete without music. Singing and dancing, caroling and playing joyous music, commemorative hymns, processionals, parades, and fanfares—each and all herald special days and occasions for people of all ages.

In the "me," "my," and "you" and "yours" preoccupations in early years with personal affections, the most important day of all is "*my* birthday." Next comes Christmas, which also celebrates the birthday of a child, and in love and devotion to the Holy Babe thousands of songs are sung by old and young together. There is no better and happier way for children to learn the best-loved carols. Smaller children will learn neither all the words of a stanza nor all the stanzas of a given song, but they will learn enough of their favorites to "catch rides"

when singing with older boys and girls and with grown-ups.

The same is true of patriotic songs. Just because the whole of "The Star-Spangled Banner," "America," and "America the Beautiful" is too much for little folks does not mean that they should be deprived of joining in the singing of these songs when and where they can. Frequently one of the Christmas or patriotic songs will be given as *my* favorite song by a kindergartener. The youngest of these children are often highly susceptible to the spirit embodied in the most grown-up of songs. This is particularly true when the associations connected with festival songs are such that children are carried into a depth of feeling that lies beyond understanding.

Please, everybody, look at me!
Today I'm five years old, you see!
And after this I won't be four,
Not ever, ever, any more!

I won't be three—or two—or one,
For that was when I'd first begun.
Now I'll be five for a while, and then
I'll be something else again.

Mary Louise Allen

My Birthday Is Today

L.B.P.

Folk Tune

Happy Birthday

German Folk Tune

Hap-py Birth-day, Hap-py Birth-day, Hap-py Birth-day to you. Hap-py
(Bill Simms.)

Birth-day, Hap-py Birth-day, Hap-py Birth-day to you. Hap-py

Birth-day, Hap - py Birth-day, Hap - py Birth-day to you.

Birthday March

Joseph Joachim Raff

From "Lenore Symphony"

Tempo di marcia

A lively, lilting, and joyous rhythm for marching around a birthday cake or to the refreshment table, or for a parade in honor of the "birthday child" of the day.

72

Halloween

Halloween Is Coming

Children's Song

Oh, Hal - low-een is com - ing, Hal - low-een is com - ing, Oh,

Hal - low-een is com - ing, Oh, what fun.

Said a pumpkin to me,
"I'd rather be
A lantern for all
The world to see!"

"With a mouth a-smile
All, all the while,
I'd fright the dark
For many a mile!"

Amanda Barris

See My Big Eyes

Spooky

See my big and scar - y eyes. Look out now, a big sur-prise!(*Boo!*)

Boo!

Oo - oo-oo - oo - oo - oo - oo, I'm look-ing right at you. (*Boo!*)

73

Nocturne

H. Reinhold

Imitative Play: (1) Pretend to be gnomes with short bodies, large heads, and big feet that go "clop-clop." They carry heavy packs on their bent shoulders. This makes them swing from side to side as they move stealthily along. (2) Gnomes digging in the earth for treasure, then hammering gold and silver into presents for good children.

Dramatization: The weird and spooky mood of this music suggests stories and pantomime about mysterious creatures: dwarfs, gnomes, leprechauns, and hobgoblins with the mysterious goings on of a Halloween night. It may serve as background for acting out either imagined or familiar stories. For example, children like to pantomime the dwarfs going to work in "Snow White and the Seven Dwarfs," or "Rumpelstiltskin" stamping his right foot on the ground so hard that he couldn't pull it out, so hopped away on his left foot, howling with rage.

I'm a Jack-o'-lantern

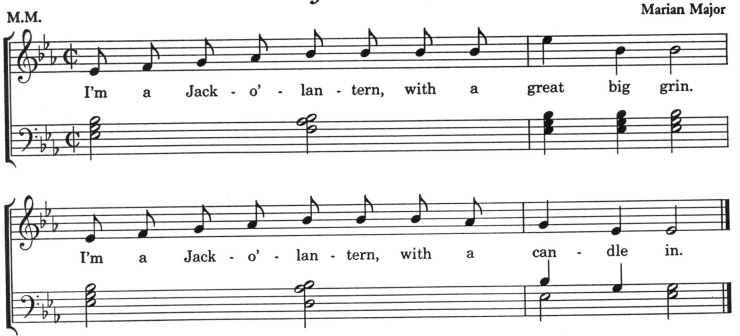

I'm a Jack-o'-lan-tern, with a great big grin.

I'm a Jack-o'-lan-tern, with a can-dle in.

See page 13, "Gigue," Corelli.
At Halloween time children like to skip to the field to pick pumpkins.
See page 20, "Tiptoe March," Italian Folk.
Good rhythm and mood for Jack-o'-lantern parade.

Halloween Has Come

Louella Garrett

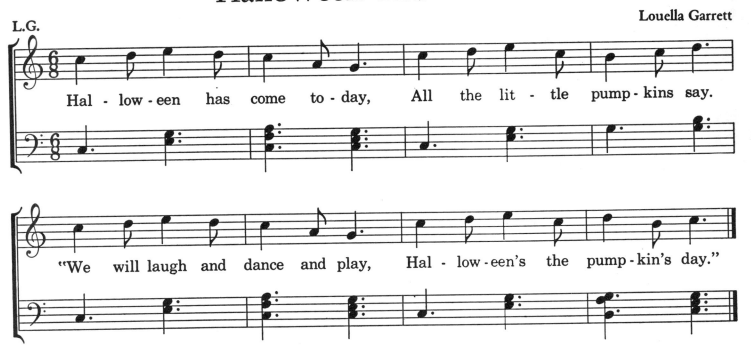

Hal-low-een has come to-day, All the lit-tle pump-kins say.

"We will laugh and dance and play, Hal-low-een's the pump-kin's day."

Listening and Dramatization: "Gnomes," Reinhold. Hear recording in Victor
Rhythm Album One. The music suggests the mischievous frolicking of the
mysterious folk of Halloween. Children could pretend to steal from house to
house and scare people with false faces and spooky costumes.

75

Thanksgiving

Thanksgiving Is Coming

Children's Song

Thanks - giv - ing is com - ing, I'm glad. Thanks-

giv - ing is com - ing, I'm glad!

Company Is Coming

S.B.

Sally Bowen

Com-p'ny is com-ing to - day, . Com-p'ny is com-ing to - day.

All of our cou-sins and un-cles and aunts, Com-p'ny is com-ing to - day. .

A Big Fat Turkey

Kansas City School Children

A big fat tur-key said one day, Gob-ble, gob-ble, gob-ble, gob-ble, gob-ble.

76

Gobble, Gobble

Susan Castle

He's big and fat and gob-ble, gob-ble, gob-bles, He spreads his tail and gob-ble, gob-ble, gob-bles, But when Thanks-giv-ing Day is here, Then it's our turn to gob-ble, gob-ble, gob-ble.

Prayer

Marian Major

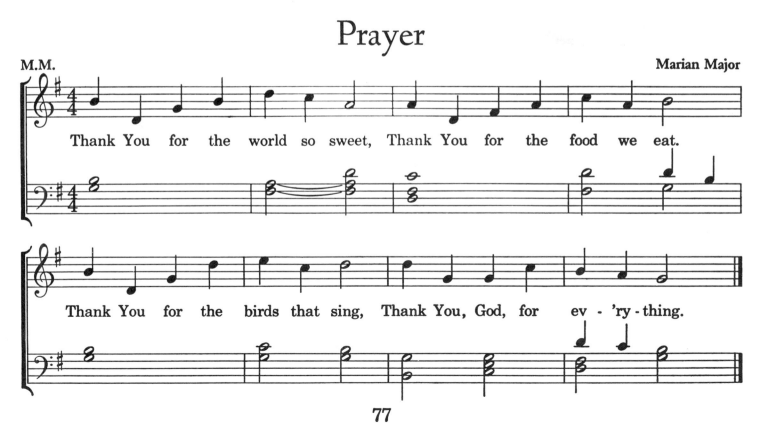

Thank You for the world so sweet, Thank You for the food we eat. Thank You for the birds that sing, Thank You, God, for ev-'ry-thing.

Christmas

Little fairy snowflakes
    Dancing in the flue;
Old Mr. Santa Claus,
    What is keeping you?
Twilight and firelight
    Shadows come and go;

Merry chime of sleigh-bells
    Twinkling through the snow.
Mother's knitting stockings,
    Pussy's got the ball.
Don't you think that Christmas
    Is the nicest time of all?

Unknown

Bells of Christmas

M.R.

Moiselle Renstrom

Jing-a-ling-a-ling, jing-a-ling-a-ling, Hear the bells of Christ-mas ring.

BELL DANCE *(Have children play this rhythm with sleigh bells.)*

Play an octave higher than written.

Christmas Song

Eugene Field[1]

Folk Tune

Why do bells of Christ-mas ring? Ding, ding, ding, ding, ding, ding!

Why do lit-tle chil-dren sing? Sing, sing, sing!

[1]Reprinted from *Sharps and Flats*, Vol. II, by Eugene Field; copyright 1900, 1901, 1928 by Julia
Sutherland Field; used by permission of the publishers, Charles Scribner's Sons.

The Angels

Kansas City School Children

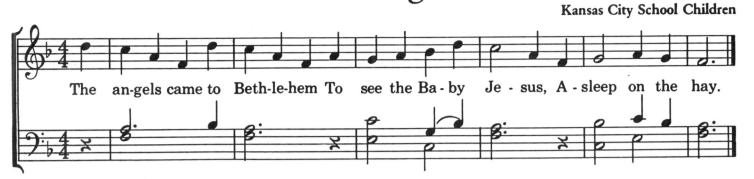

The an-gels came to Beth-le-hem To see the Ba-by Je-sus, A-sleep on the hay.

O Little Town of Bethlehem

Phillips Brooks

Lewis H. Redner

O lit-tle town of Beth-le-hem, How still we see thee lie, A-

bove thy deep and dream-less sleep The si-lent stars go by; Yet

in thy dark streets shin-eth The ev-er-last-ing light, The

hopes and fears of all the years Are met in thee to-night.

Away in a Manger

Martin Luther

1. A - way in a man - ger, no crib for His bed, The
2. The cat - tle are low - ing, the Ba - by a - wakes, But

lit - tle Lord Je - sus laid down His sweet head. The
lit - tle Lord Je - sus no cry - ing He makes. I

stars in the sky looked down where He lay. The
love Thee, Lord Je - sus! Look down from the sky, And

lit - tle Lord Je - sus a - sleep in the hay.
stay by my cra - dle till morn - ing is nigh.

Chimes of Christmas

Softly struck gong

Kitten's Christmas Song

L.B.P.

Polish

Sleep, sleep, Ba-by, sleep, Ba-by Je-sus go to sleep, go to sleep.

Stroke my clean and soft warm fur While I lie so still and purr.

See the story in *Lullaby or Why Pussy Washes His Face So Often*, by Josephine Bernhard, published by Roy Publishing Company, New York, New York.

Silent Night

Joseph Mohr

Franz Gruber

Si - lent night, Ho - ly night! All is calm, all is bright

Round yon Vir - gin Moth-er and Child. Ho - ly In-fant so ten-der and mild,

Sleep in heav-en-ly peace, Sleep · in heav-en-ly peace.

Greeting Song

German Folk Tune

Mer-ry Christ-mas, Mer-ry Christ-mas, Mer-ry Christ-mas to you. Mer-ry

Christ-mas, Mer-ry Christ-mas, Mer-ry Christ-mas to you. Mer-ry

Christ-mas, Mer - ry Christ-mas, Mer - ry Christ-mas to you.

Jingle Bells

J. Pierpont

Jin - gle bells! Jin - gle bells! Jin - gle all the way!

Oh, what fun it is to ride in a one - horse o - pen sleigh!

Jingle Bells (Continued)

Jin - gle bells! Jin - gle bells! Jin - gle all the way!

Oh, what fun it is to ride in a one - horse o - pen sleigh!

Santa's Helpers

Kansas City School Children

Tap, tap, tap, tap, Go our lit - tle ham - mers.
(Rhythm sticks and wood-blocks)

Ring, ring, ring, ring, Go our lit - tle bells. We are San - ta's help - ers.
(Triangles)

Tap - a - tap - a - tap - tap. We are San - ta's help - ers Mak - ing Christ - mas toys.
(Rhythm sticks and wood-blocks)

Let's Dance Around the Christmas Tree

A.W.

Angela Wiechard

Let's dance a-round the Christ-mas tree, Heigh-ho, heigh-ho! Let's

dance a-round the Christ-mas tree, Heigh-ho, heigh-ho! We'll

skip a-round, a-round, and round, Tra la la la la la! Let's

dance a-round the Christ-mas tree, Heigh-ho, heigh-ho!

Christmas Tree March

Niels Gade, Op. 36

Children enjoy a processional around a Christmas tree Each child may
carry a wreath, candle, sprig of holly, a star, or some other decoration as they
march.

This music is appropriate to use when one is carrying offerings to a
miniature crèche.

Valentine Day

"My love for you will never fail
As long as pussy has a tail."

The Rooster Crows

A Valentine for You

L.B.P.

French

1. In my hand is a val - en - tine, In my hand is a val - en -
2. Guess which hand holds the val - en - tine, Guess which hand holds the val - en -

tine, In which hand is the val - en - tine, In which hand is the val - en - tine?
tine. If you guess, then it is for you. If you guess, then it is for you.

When You Send a Valentine

Mildred J. Hill

Louella Garrett

When you send a val - en - tine, That's the time for fun. *(Xylophone)* Push it un - der-

neath the door, Ring the bell and run, run, run, run! Ring the bell and run!
(Triangle) *(Triangle)* *(Xylophone)*

Our Country

America

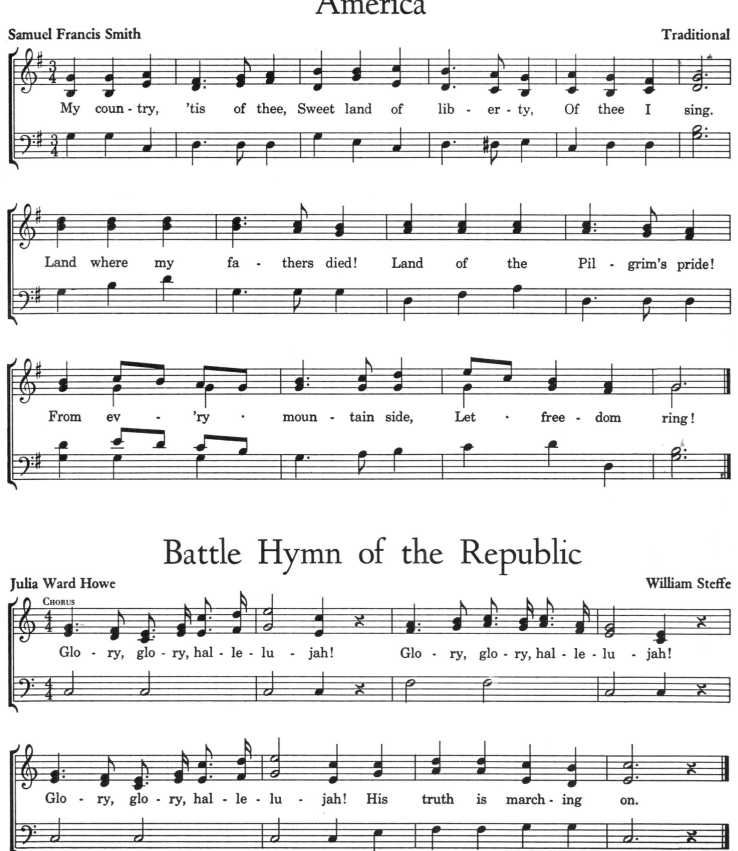

Samuel Francis Smith — Traditional

My coun - try, 'tis of thee, Sweet land of lib - er - ty, Of thee I sing.

Land where my fa - thers died! Land of the Pil - grim's pride!

From ev - 'ry moun - tain side, Let free - dom ring!

Battle Hymn of the Republic

Julia Ward Howe — William Steffe

CHORUS

Glo - ry, glo - ry, hal - le - lu - jah! Glo - ry, glo - ry, hal - le - lu - jah!

Glo - ry, glo - ry, hal - le - lu - jah! His truth is march - ing on.

The Star-Spangled Banner

Francis Scott Key

John Stafford Smith

Oh, say! can you see, by the dawn's ear - ly light, What so proud - ly we

hailed at the twi-light's last gleam-ing, Whose broad stripes and bright stars, through the

per - i - lous fight O'er the ram-parts we watched were so gal - lant - ly

stream-ing? And the rock-ets' red glare, the bombs burst-ing in air, Gave

proof through the night that our flag was still there. Oh, say does that Star-span-gled

The Star-Spangled Banner (Continued)

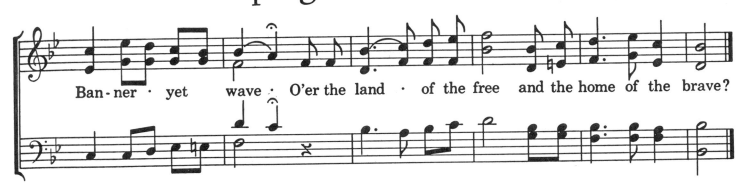

Ban-ner · yet wave · O'er the land · of the free and the home of the brave?

Yankee Doodle

Traditional

1. Yan-kee Doo-dle went to town A rid-ing on a po-ny, He
2. There was Cap-tain Wash-ing-ton Up-on a slap-ping stal-lion, A-

stuck a feath-er in his hat And called it mac-a-ro-ni.
giv-ing or-ders to his men; I guess there was a mil-lion.

Chorus

Yan-kee Doo-dle keep it up, Yan-kee Doo-dle dan-dy,

Mind the mu-sic and the step, And with the girls be han-dy.

89

Out on the breeze,
O'er land and seas,
A beautiful banner is streaming.

Shining its stars,
Splendid its bars,
Under the sunshine 'tis gleaming.

Hail to the flag,
The dear, bonny flag—
The flag that is red, white, and blue.

Lydia Avery Coonley Ward

America the Beautiful

Katharine Lee Bates

Samuel A. Ward

O beau-ti-ful for spa-cious skies, For am-ber waves of grain, For

pur-ple moun-tain maj-es-ties A-bove the fruit-ed plain! . . A-

mer-i-ca! A-mer-i-ca! God shed His grace on thee, And

crown thy good with broth-er-hood, From sea to shin-ing sea!

Easter

O bells in the steeple,
Ring out to all people
That Easter is here!

May Riley Smith

Easter

Louella Garrett

Ding, dong, ding, dong, The East - er bells ring. Ding,

dong, ding, dong, The East - er bells sing.

Easter Bells

Sue Hanlin

Voice

High in the church tow'r the East - er bells ring,

Piano

Ding ding dong, ding ding dong, ding ding dong, ding.

Listening: "Legend of the Bells," from Chimes of Normandy. (Victor Listening Album One.)

Easter Duck and Easter Chick

Elsie Parrish

James Barton

East-er duck and East-er chick, East-er eggs with choc-'late thick,

East-er hats for one and all, East-er bun-ny makes a call!

Hap-py East-er al-ways brings Such a lot of pleas-ant things.

I Am Bunny Pink Ears

M.R.

Moiselle Renstrom

Bunny brings his gift

I am Bun-ny Pink Ears. How do you do? Here's an East-er bas-ket

The children sing,

I have brought to you. Thank you, thank you, Pret-ty East-er Bun-ny.

Imitative Play· Hopping like rabbits. (See page 19, ''The Rabbit,'' Gounod.)

92

ABOUT THE WONDERFUL OUTSIDE WORLD

The world is so full
Of a number of things
I'm sure we should all
Be as happy as kings.

Robert Louis Stevenson

The world of nature is an unending source of joy to children. They feel intimately related to earth, sun, air, and water. Animals, insects, and all growing things are friends. Then children are insatiably curious about such matters as: What makes fire? Where does the wind come from? What makes grass green? Why the rain, the snow, the thunder?

Despite the intensity of this deeply personal interest in natural phenomena which is present in childhood, child-like nature songs are not plentiful. Observation of children shows that they *act with* nature considerably more than they talk about its beauties and wonders. Children *bask* or *run* in the sun; they *blow* with the wind and *float* with clouds; they *splash* and *splatter* in water and *squish* and *squash* in mud and slush; and snow provides a whole new and magical world for play and investigation. All this shows that *action* is the child's expression of what he *senses* about the world at large. Because children sense the quality of things acutely, they act out what they feel until it becomes a part of conscious living and learning.

The manifold patterns of sound and movement, which make a singing world of the universe, offer a profusion of delights to the eager ears and voices of children. They love to howl and roar like the wind; they enjoy inventing word sounds that describe falling rain and leaves and snow; and there is no animal, bird, or insect voice that they do not try to imitate.

Sensitivity to, and interest in, the tonal and rhythmic patterns of music can be increased and guided more effectively by making use of a child's natural desire to imitate every sound and movement that he hears and sees. Recognizing relationships between singing and the tones produced in imitative play is particularly helpful to indifferent as well as timid singers.

A so-called "nonsinger" may be observed at play roaring like a lion, like the wind, or like the engine of an airplane. And we may be sure of this: if a child can run the tonal gamut required for his expert imitations (and they are expert) of these things, *he is no monotone!* All that such a child needs is help in forming a connecting link between the ordinary expressive uses of his voice and what happens when he uses it in song.

When left to follow their own intuitions, children feel music to be a quality of experience, adding intensity to the whole world of sense, which they so ceaselessly explore. They sing with the birds, buzz with bees, chirp with crickets, cackle with hens, walk like elephants, roar like lions, "chug" like tugboats, and "whirr" like airplanes. It doesn't matter—anything and everything, just to find what creatures, people, and things are "like." And children's efforts to identify themselves with all sounding and moving things give them a natural starting point for finding out *what music is "like."*

See pages xiii–xv, *Creative Activities.*

94

About the Sun
and Moon
and Stars

Now the sun has gone to sleep,
And birds are in their nest;
So I will thank You for my day—
My busy day of work and play—
And then I'll go to rest.

Eliz. McE. Shields

Take My Hand

M.M.

Marian Major

Take my hand and we will run With the wind out in the sun.

The Sun

M.M.

Marian Major

1. The sun's a light that lights the day, And when it's night, it goes a-way.
2. The moon's a light that lights the night, And when it's day, it's out of sight.

The Happy Stars

J.E.G.

James Edwin Green

The stars in the heav-ens are twin-kling, you see, I

think they are hap-py and wink-ing at me.

The Stars

L.G.

Louella Garrett

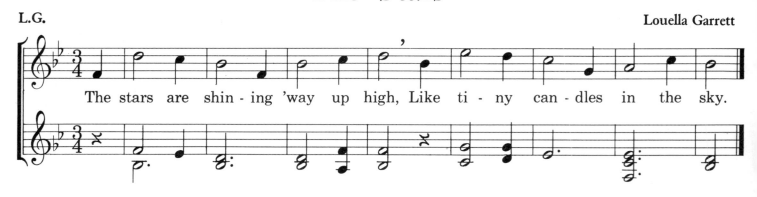

The stars are shin-ing 'way up high, Like ti-ny can-dles in the sky.

I See the Moon

Celtic Child's Saying

L.B.P.

Quietly

I see the moon, and the moon sees me. God bless the moon and God bless me.

The Man in the Moon

From "Poems for Children's Hour"

Sue Hanlin

Not too fast

The man in the moon looked out of the moon, Looked

out of the moon and said, "'Tis time for all chil-dren

on the earth To think a-bout get-ting to bed!"

pp

About Wind and Weather

Oh, oh, how the wild winds blow!

Like a Leaf

Unknown   Folk Tune

Like a leaf or a feath-er In the wind-y, wind-y weath-er, We will

whirl a-round and twirl a-round And all fall down to-geth-er.

Imitative Play: "Waltz," Brahms. Blowing with the wind. See page 31. (Victor Rhythm Album Two.)

Listening: "Valse Gracieuse," Dvořák. (1) Gentle breeze; (2) noisy wind. (Victor Rhythm Album Three.)

Spit, Spat, Spatter

L.B.P.   L.B.P.

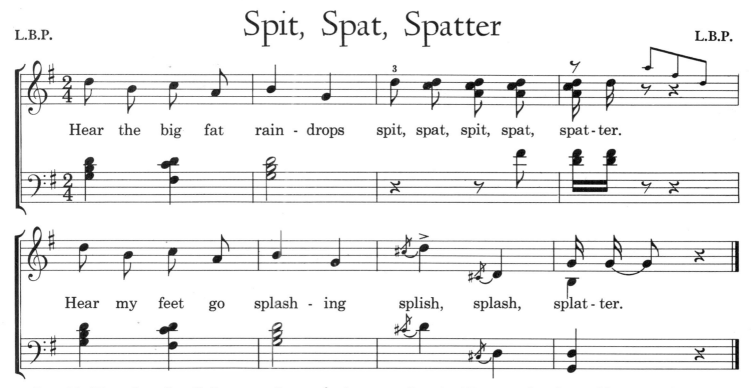

Hear the big fat rain-drops spit, spat, spit, spat, spat-ter.

Hear my feet go splash-ing splish, splash, splat-ter.

Page 11, "Run, Run, Run," Concone. Patter of rain-drops, fingers, rain rattles.

Page 16, "Sicilienne," Gluck. Pulling and squashing in rain and mud.

Page 14, "Happy and Light," Balfe. Merry play of rain-drops. Fingers playing lightly on desks are good for making rain effects. Rain rattles are appropriate also as accompaniments to rain songs and instrumental selections.

Under My Umbrella

Children's Song

Spit, spat, spat - ter On my big um - brel - la.

See me walk - ing With my big um - brel - la.

Oh, Isn't It Fun!

M.M.

Marian Major

Oh, is - 'nt it fun when the rain comes down O - ver the park and

o - ver the town.

DANCE
8 va.

Listening: "Etude Joy-euse," Kopylow. (Victor Rhythm Album One.) Imitate pattering raindrops with (1) light hand claps; (2) rhythm sticks; (3) rain rattles.

Rain

Traditional

Folk Tune

1. Rain, rain, go a - way, Come a - gain some oth - er day.
2. Rain, rain, go a - way, Lit - tle Su - sie wants to play.
John - ny

Autumn

"Come, little leaves," said the wind one day,
"Come over the meadows with me and play.
Put on your dresses of red and gold;
For summer is gone, and the days grow cold."

George Cooper

The Wind Is Singing

Nora Belle Emerson

N.B.E.

The wind is sing-ing a love-ly song To the leaves the whole day long, "Oh,

come with me, we shall dance and play, So wear your col-ors bright and gay."

The Leaves

Louella Garrett

Margaret P. Sutphen

The leaves are drop-ping from the trees, Yel-low, brown and red. They

faster

pat-ter soft-ly like the rain. One land-ed on my head!

Down, Down

Eleanor Farjeon[1]

L.B.P.

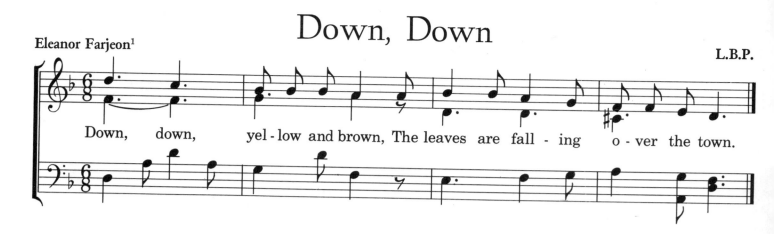

Down, down, yel-low and brown, The leaves are fall-ing o-ver the town.

Valse Serenade

E. Poldini

Imitative Play: Picking autumn leaves and putting them in a basket; raking leaves; picking apples and pears; gathering nuts. (Victor Rhythm Album One.)

Winter

I'm Glad It's Snowing

Children's Chant

1. I'm glad it's snow-ing, snow-ing, snow-ing. I'm glad it's snow-ing, snow-ing snow.
2. I can throw snow-balls, snow-balls, snow-balls. I can throw snow-balls in the snow.
3. I can go crunch-ing, crunch-ing, crunch-ing. I can go crunch-ing in the snow.

Walking in the Snow • (Wheelbarrow Motive)

Clara Louise Anderson

Heavily

Imitative Play: Walking in snow or slush with galoshes on. (Victor Rhythm Album One.)

The Snowman

F.C.

Florence Calahan

I like to make a snow-ball And roll it on the ground. It

grows in-to a snow-man So big and fat and round.

Without a Sound at All

Grace B. Haynes

Henry M. Halvorson

With - out a sound at all, As soft - ly as can be The

snow - flakes start to fall Up - on the earth and me.

Skaters' Dance

Cornelius Gurlitt

For suggestions see page 31, "Waltz," Brahms, Op. 39, No. 2. (Victor Rhythm Album Two.)

Spring

In the heart of a seed
Buried deep, so deep,
A dear little plant
Lay fast asleep.

"Wake!" said the sunshine,
"And creep to the light."
"Wake!" said the voice
Of the raindrops bright.

The little plant heard,
And it rose to see
What the wonderful
Outside world might be.

Kate Louise Brown

A Little Seed

Wilhelmina Seegmiller

Sue Hanlin

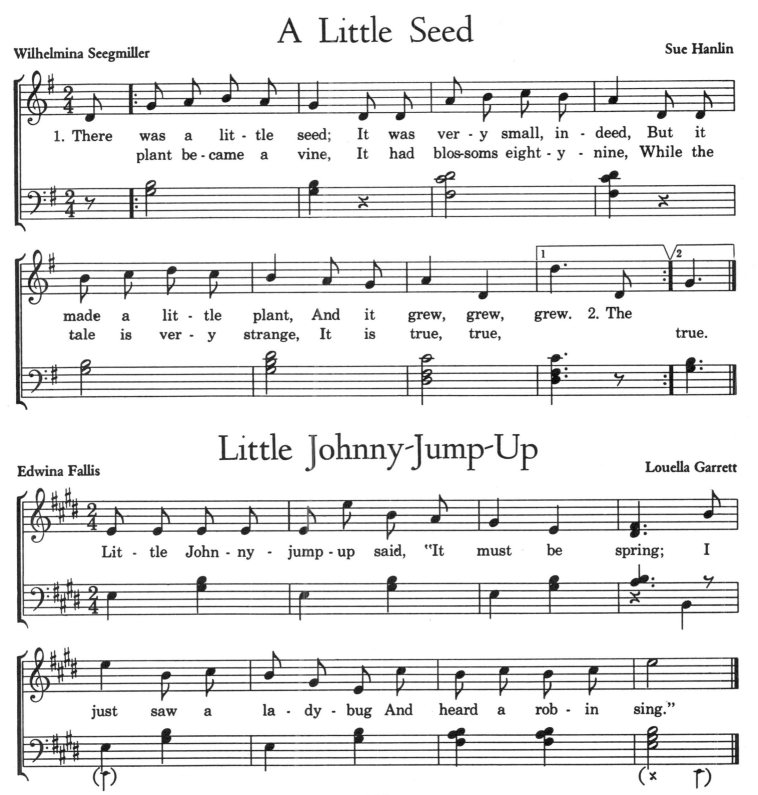

1. There was a lit-tle seed; It was ver-y small, in-deed, But it
plant be-came a vine, It had blos-soms eight-y-nine, While the

made a lit-tle plant, And it grew, grew, grew. 2. The
tale is ver-y strange, It is true, true, true.

Little Johnny-Jump-Up

Edwina Fallis

Louella Garrett

Lit-tle John-ny-jump-up said, "It must be spring; I

just saw a la-dy-bug And heard a rob-in sing."

103

Nature's Dream • (Arabesque)

G. Karganoff

Children roll up in balls, pretending to be seeds. As music moves out and up, they unfold gradually. First one arm, then the other, reaches out and pushes up. Then the head is lifted. They kneel, finally growing up to standing position. Dramatizing the various stages of growth in plants and flowers prepares children to use their bodies more imaginatively in expressing what they see and feel.

About Birds and Bees and Bugs

All things bright and beautiful,
All creatures great and small,
All things wise and wonderful,
The Lord God made them all.

Cecil Frances Alexander

A Blue Bird Sings

M.R.

Moiselle Renstrom

1. I'm a lit - tle bird of blue, Tweet, tweet, tweet, tweet, tweet.
2. I will sing a song for you, Tweet, tweet, tweet, tweet, tweet.

A Bird in a Pear Tree

Nursery Rhyme

English

1. A bird sat in a pear tree, Heigh - o, heigh - o, heigh - o! A
2. A bird sat on a pear tree And sang, "Tweet, tweet, tweet, tweet." A

bird sat in a pear tree And up and down did go.
bird sat on a pear tree And sang his song so sweet.

Flying Birds

Clara Louise Anderson

This music tells about birds on the wing. Children should be encouraged to watch birds, then imitate what they see. It helps, also, to learn some of the words which describe flying motions: soaring, dipping, wheeling or circling, fluttering, swerving, etc. (Victor Rhythm Album One.)

106

Birdling · (Vöglein)

Edvard Grieg, Op. 43, No. 4

This music tells about birds singing, not about birds in flight. First, children should listen quietly to the twitter and trills of this lovely bird music. Later, they may like to pretend to sing like happy birds as they ride up and down on the leafy limb of a tree.

Listening: "In a Bird Store," M. L. Lake. (Decca Album "Animal Pictures in Music.")

Busy, Buzzy Bee

Children's Song

Bus - y, buzz - y, bus - y bee, Buzz - ing round from tree to tree.

Bus - y, buzz - y, bus - y bee, Don't you dare to buzz near me.

Listening: "The Bee," Schubert. (Victor Listening Album Three.)

107

My Pretty Butterfly

L.B.P.

L.B.P.

See him fly - ing high, · Pret - ty but - ter - fly, · ·

Wing-ing, wing-ing high, · · Fly and touch the sky. · · ·

Papillons No. 8

Robert Schumann, Op. 2

Free Play: Swinging, swaying, rocking with body and arms; running lightly with outspread arms.

Imitative Play: Fly and flutter like butterflies. Let the music tell when wings are folded, when they flutter and fan, when they are spread in flight. (See pages xvi–xvii for using scarves for wings, *Apparatus, Materials, and Properties.*)

Victor Rhythm Album Three.

108

Little black bug,
Little black bug,
Where have you been?

Little Bug

I've been under the rug,
Said the little black bug.
Bug—ug—ug—ug.

Margaret Wise Brown

Oh, lit - tle bug, oh, lit - tle bug, Why do you leave your rug - ug - ug? It

is a nice warm sun - ny day, So I came out to play - ay - ay.

Cricket

James Tippett

Paul Forde

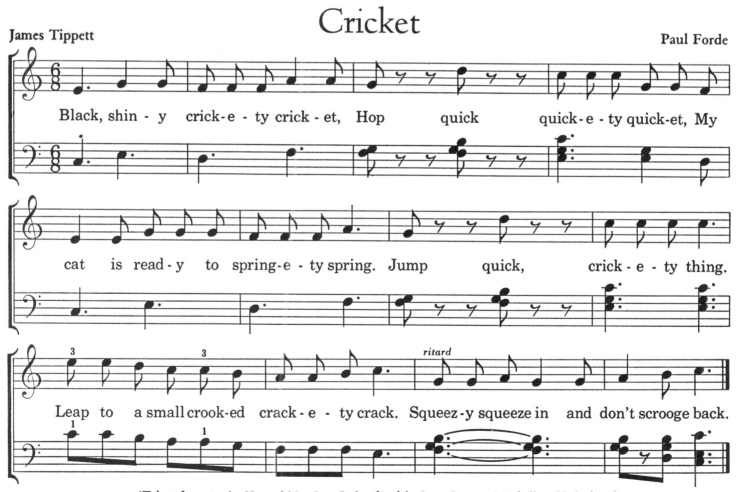

Black, shin - y crick - e - ty crick - et, Hop quick quick - e - ty quick-et, My

cat is read - y to spring - e - ty spring. Jump quick, crick - e - ty thing.

Leap to a small crook - ed crack - e - ty crack. Squeez-y squeeze in and don't scrooge back.

[1]Taken from *Another Here and Now Story Book*, edited by Lucy Sprague Mitchell, published and copyright 1937 by E. P. Dutton & Co., Inc., New York.

About Our Pets

If I had a hundred dollars to spend,
Or maybe a little more,
I'd hurry as fast as my legs would go
Straight to the animal store.

I wouldn't say, "How much for this or that?
What kind of a dog is he?"
I'd buy as many as rolled an eye
Or waggled a tail at me!

Rachel Field

Doggy and Kitty

Angela Wiechard

A.W.

Dog - gie says to Kit - ty, "Bow - wow - wow."

Kit - ty says to Dog - gie, "Me - ow, me - ow, me - ow."

My Kitty

Children's Song

My kit - ty has green eyes, My kit - ty has short ears, My

kit - ty has fine whis - kers And a long and fur - ry tail.

Kitty—Pretty

Lady Bell

From "Singing Circle"

Kit, Kit, Kit, Kit-ty, Kit-ty, Kit - ty. Prit, prit, prit, pret-ty, pret-ty, pret - ty.

Listening: "Capering Kittens," Rudolf Ganz. (Decca Album "Animal Pictures in Music.")

My Pony Bill

A.W.

Angela Wiechard

My Po - ny Bill is rid - ing high, See my po - ny gal-lop-ing by, My

Po - ny Bill is rid - ing high, See him gal - lop - ing by.

Peter Rabbit

M.M.

Marian Major

Pe-ter Rab - bit lost his jack - et, Pe-ter Rab - bit lost his shoes, Pe - ter

Rab - bit dis - o - beyed ma - ma, And that we can't ex - cuse.

Here Comes Our Rabbit

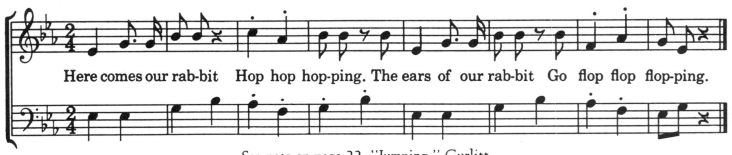

Here comes our rab-bit Hop hop hop-ping. The ears of our rab-bit Go flop flop flop-ping.

See note on page 22, "Jumping," Gurlitt.

Puppy's Tail

Unknown

Susan Castle

See my hap-py pup-py's tail, Wig-gle, wag-gle, wig-gle, wag-gle.

"I like you," it says to me, Wig-gle, wag-gle, wig-gle, wag-gle.

Two Little Kitty-Cats

Old Rhyme

L.B.P.

Two lit-tle kit-ty-cats ly-ing in the sun, One jumped up and said, "I'd like to run."

Then said the oth-er, "I'll run too. Run-ning round and round and round, I'll play with you."

Dramatization: Two children are chosen to play the part of the kitty-cats while the others sing.

Kitty Cat

Translated

Polish Folk Song

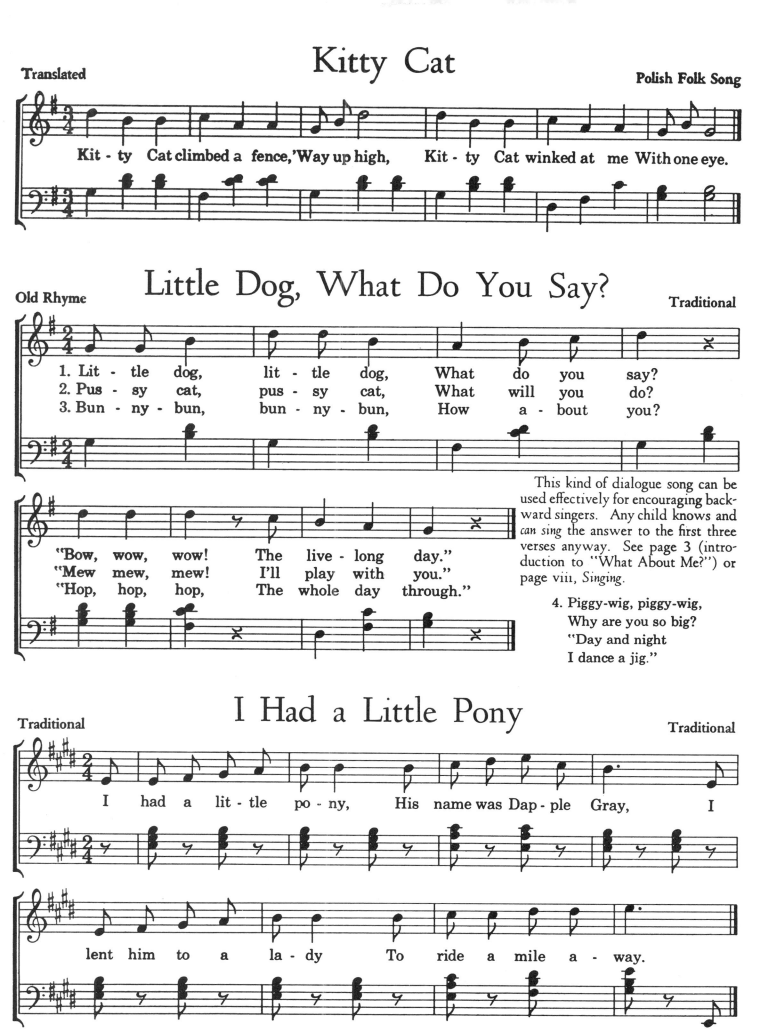

Kit - ty Cat climbed a fence, 'Way up high, Kit - ty Cat winked at me With one eye.

Little Dog, What Do You Say?

Old Rhyme

Traditional

1. Lit - tle dog, lit - tle dog, What do you say?
2. Pus - sy cat, pus - sy cat, What will you do?
3. Bun - ny - bun, bun - ny - bun, How a - bout you?

"Bow, wow, wow! The live - long day."
"Mew mew, mew! I'll play with you."
"Hop, hop, hop, The whole day through."

This kind of dialogue song can be used effectively for encouraging backward singers. Any child knows and *can sing* the answer to the first three verses anyway. See page 3 (introduction to "What About Me?") or page viii, *Singing*.

4. Piggy-wig, piggy-wig,
Why are you so big?
"Day and night
I dance a jig."

I Had a Little Pony

Traditional

Traditional

I had a lit - tle po - ny, His name was Dap - ple Gray, I

lent him to a la - dy To ride a mile a - way.

113

About Farm Animals

I love to go to see Aunt Flo
And chase her old fat hen
That wobbles all around the yard
Again and then again!

I love to watch the piggies eat
And hear the horses neigh,
And run the little calves a race
And slide down stacks of hay.

Ruth Edna Stanton

A Getting-up Song

Lady Bell

From "Singing Circle"

1. When ducks get up in the morn - ing They al - ways say, "Good day," When
2. When pigs get up in the morn - ing They al - ways say, "Good day," When
3. When sheep get up in the morn - ing They al - ways say, "Good day," When

ducks get up in the morn - ing They al - ways say, "Good day."
pigs get up in the morn - ing They al - ways say, "Good day."
sheep get up in the morn - ing They al - ways say, "Good day."

Quack! Quack! Quack! Quack! That is what they say, they say,
Oink! Oink! Oink! Oink! That is what they say, they say,
Baa! Baa! Baa! Baa! That is what they say, they say,

Quack! Quack! Quack! Quack! That is what they say.
Oink! Oink! Oink! Oink! That is what they say.
Baa! Baa! Baa! Baa! That is what they say.

4. When cows get up in the morning
   They always say, "Good day,"
   When cows get up in the morning
   They always say, "Good day."
   Moo! Moo! Moo! Moo!
   That is what they say, they say,
   Moo! Moo! Moo! Moo!
   That is what they say.

5. When we get up in the morning
   We always say, "Good day,"
   When we get up in the morning
   We always say, "Good day."
   Hello! Hello! Hello! Hello!
   That is what we say, we say,
   Hello! Hello! Hello! Hello!
   That is what we say.

Mrs. Hen and Little Chick

S.H.

Sue Hanlin

1. Mis-sus Hen says, "Cluck cluck, come here.   You must learn to scratch, my dear."
2. Mis-sus Hen says, "Cluck cluck, watch me!   Here's the way to scratch, you see."

Lit-tle Chick says, "Peep peep, I will,   I'll catch a big worm in my bill."
Lit-tle Chick says, "Peep peep, it's fun,   I'll try to catch the big-gest one."

Listening: "Etincelles," Moszkowski, Op. 36, No. 6. (Victor Rhythm Album One.)
Imitative Play: Little chickens running and pecking.

I Went for a Ride in the Country

F.C.

Florence Calahan

I went for a ride in the coun-try   And what do you think I saw?   I

saw a don-key eat-ing grass. Hee-haw! Hee-haw! Hee-haw!

115

Mary Had a Little Lamb

Sara J. Hale

Traditional

1. Ma - ry had a lit - tle lamb, Lit - tle lamb, lit - tle lamb,
2. Ev - 'ry-where that Ma - ry went, Ma - ry went, Ma - ry went,

Ma - ry had a lit - tle lamb, Its fleece was white as snow.
Ev - 'ry-where that Ma - ry went, The lamb was sure to go.

Say what you like,
All things love me!
Horse, Cow, and Mouse,
Bird, Moth, and Bee.

W. H. Davies

Thank You, Pretty Bossy-Cow

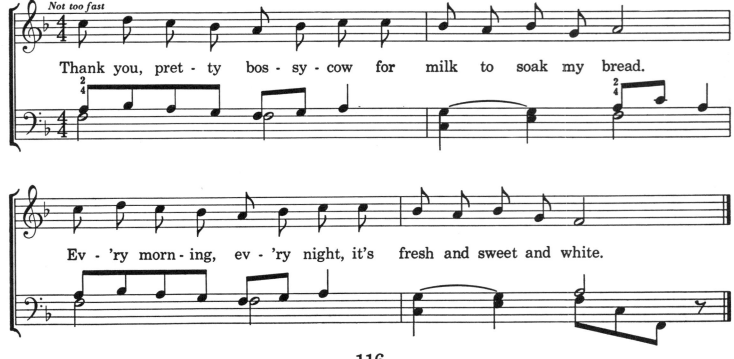

Not too fast

Thank you, pret - ty bos - sy-cow for milk to soak my bread.

Ev - 'ry morn - ing, ev - 'ry night, it's fresh and sweet and white.

My Black Hen

Nursery Rhyme

Susan Castle

Hick - e - ty pick - e - ty my black hen, She lays eggs for gen - tle - men,

Some - times nine and some - times ten, Hick - e - ty pick - e - ty my black hen.

Six Little Mice

Mother Goose

English Folk Song

1. Six lit - tle mice sat down to spin, Puss - y passed by and
2. "Shall I come in and bite off your threads?" "Oh, no, Miss Puss - y, you'll

she peeped in, "What are you at, my lit - tle men?"
bite off our heads." "Oh, no, I won't, I'll help you spin."

"Mak - ing good coats for gen - tle - men."
"That may be so, but you can't come in."

Listening: "The Cat and the Mouse," Aaron Copland. (Decca Album "Animal Pictures in Music.") "Spinning Song," Kullak (Victor Listening Album Two).

Dramatize: Class are the mice while children take turns playing the part of Pussy. Children could pantomime story of "Six Little Mice" to *Spinning Song* music. The first and last sections describe the whirling wheel. Children can make over and over movements of hands for the rhythmic whir of spinning. The contrasting middle section of the music is quiet enough to use as background for pantomiming the visit of Pussy. After slamming the door in her face, the spinning continues until the music stops.

к

The Hen

L.B.

Lena Buck

Cut, cut, cut, cu - da - cut, Cut, cut, cut, cu - da - cut,

Cut, cut, cut, cu - da - cut, I laid an egg for mar - ket.

Little Ducky Duddle

M.R.

Moiselle Renstrom

A lit - tle Duck - y Dud - dle Went wad - ing in a pud - dle, Went

wad - ing in a pud-dle quite small. (quack, quack) Said he, "It does-n't mat-ter How

much I splash and splat-ter; I'm on - ly a duck - y aft - er all." (quack, quack)

118

About Animals
in the Zoo

When I grow up
(For I must, you know!)
I'll go wherever
I want to go—
I'll go to the Zoo
Whenever I choose.

Dorothy Brown Thompson

At the Zoo

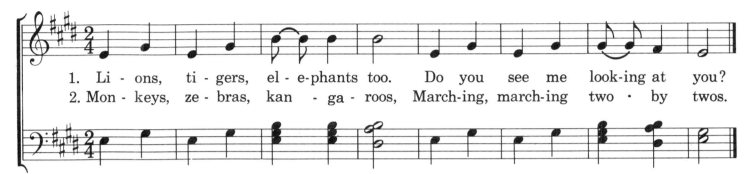

1. Li - ons, ti - gers, el - e-phants too. Do you see me look-ing at you?
2. Mon - keys, ze - bras, kan - ga - roos, March-ing, march-ing two - by twos.

Guess What We Saw at the Zoo

K.S.B.

Katherine Smith Bolt

Guess what we saw at the zoo to - day, Moth-er and Dad and me? Three

fun - ny mon-keys up in a tree, Two bears as fur - ry and white as can be,

One great big li - on who roared at me, All at the zoo to - day.

119

Lion

I am a li - on, Rrrrrr! Rrrrrr! Rrrrrr!

Monkey

I'm a lit - tle mon - key climb - ing up a tree,

If you have a pea - nut, throw it up to me.

Giraffe

Look up! Look up! If you want to see me. Look

up! Look up! I'm a tall gi - raffe.

120

Elephant

Ka-lump, ka-lump, ka-lump, ka-lump. I am an el-e-phant swing-ing my trunk.

Listening: Jumbo's Lullaby (Berceuse des Éléphants), from *Children's Corner*, Debussy. (Decca Album "Animal Pictures in Music.")

March

A. Hollaender

Free Play: Stamping, heavy walk with body lunging from side to side; slow pushing or pulling motions.

Imitative Play: The deep tones and the slow and heavy rhythmic movement of this music make it ideal for playing at being an elephant, a bear, tiger, giraffe, lion, or any other ponderous, prowling, or slow-moving animal. Children enjoy playing the game of "Tell us what you see" to this march. One child acts out whatever he imagines himself to be, while the others guess what it is. (Victor Rhythm Album Two.)

121

Bear

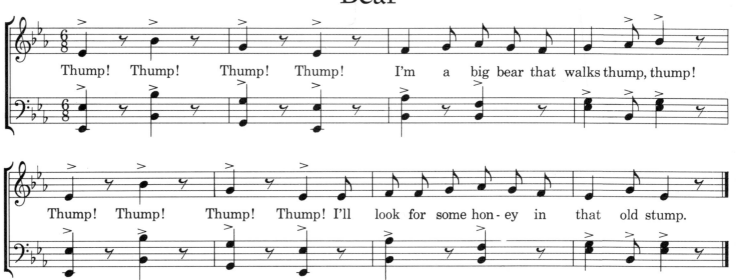

Thump! Thump! Thump! Thump! I'm a big bear that walks thump, thump!

Thump! Thump! Thump! Thump! I'll look for some hon-ey in that old stump.

Listening: "The Tame Bear," Elgar. (Victor Listening Album Two.)

Children enjoy imagining themselves to be big bears and little bears shuffling and nosing about in search of food. The little ones frolic or fight, cuffing one another with their paws. Or they prefer to be dancing bears whose keepers take them about the streets to perform and do tricks for people who put pennies in the cups hanging round the bears' necks.

Bear-Dance • (Bärentanz)

Béla Bartók, Abridged

ABOUT
THINGS THAT SING

Clocks ticking, the buzz of a bell,
Doors slamming, a happy boy's yell.

Phones ringing, the tap of a shoe,
Postman knocking, Tommy's "Yoo-hoo!"

Children laughing as they rush pell-mell
To answer the call of the dinner bell.

L. B. P.

Much that was said about sounds associated with the world of nature can be applied to music in its relation to the sounds of a man-made world of machines and mechanical devices.

Things that make fascinating and lovely sounds are music to children's ears. The *tick-tick* of daddy's watch, a telephone ringing, the buzz of a button at the door, the postman's whistle, rattling dishes, the bang of a hammer, each is enjoyed for the sake of sound aside from other interests and associations.

Then there is the enthralling music of planes and trains; trolley cars and busses; tractors and trucks; and a thousand and one things that are sources of wonder and delight to the young, who are bent upon realizing the flavor of every experience to the fullest. And the child's way of getting at what a train means in his life is to be one.

Playing train, airplane, and so on, moves easily into making up songs to accompany the movement and sounds appropriate to each. Here, again, are interests and activities that may be used to help the less musically experienced children to find themselves. (See pages iv–vi, *Individual Differences in Children's Singing.*)

A child who may be miserable and uncertain when trying to "match tones" dissociated from any meaning that he can fathom will be right at home when "choo-chooing" on a descending fourth or in "toot-tooting" on a given single tone. The sounds make sense. They have something to do with the intimate, personal concerns of children.

Songs about things that sing are made more interesting by appropriate instrumental accompaniments: *Rhythm sticks* lightly tapped for ticking clocks. *Wood-blocks*, preferably in two sizes, for the ticktock of larger clocks. A *gong* for striking the hours. A *triangle* rapidly jingled for an alarm clock's ring. A *triangle* for the telephone's ring or for the doorbell.

Children are very resourceful in thinking up and devising sound and rhythmic effects for playing train, trucks, fire engines, and the like.

About Things
We Know So Well

Tick, tock, tick, tock,
Merrily sings the clock;
It's time for work,
It's time for play,
So it sings throughout the day.
Tick, tock, tick, tock,
Merrily sings the clock.

Old Rhyme

The Clock

Alys E. Bentley

"Don't stop," says the clock, "Don't hur-ry, tick tock, Don't stop, don't hur-ry,

Tick tock tick tock tick tock tick tock tick tock tick tock."

Use rhythm sticks for "tick tock" accompaniment. Tap them lightly on back of chair or desk. The difference between tick and tock will be made more effective if the "tick" is tapped near the end of the stick and "tock" near the middle.

Listening: "The Clock," Kullak. Listen for two clocks going at the same time. A small clock says, "tick-tick-tick-tick," while a big clock says, in a slow, deep tone, "ticktock, ticktock." (Victor Rhythm Album Three.)

Telephone

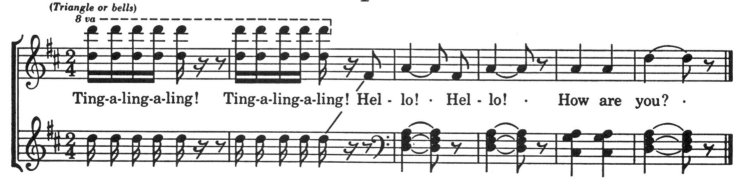

Ting-a-ling-a-ling! Ting-a-ling-a-ling! Hel-lo! · Hel-lo! · How are you? ·

Time for School

Tick, tock, tick, tock, Now it's time to go to school. Tick, tock, tick, tock, Off we go.

Playing Instruments: See page 125, "The Clock."

Rap-a-tap-tap

Traditional

Rap - a - tap - tap, tick - a - tack - too, This is the way to mend a shoe.

Shoes

DADDY'S

Click, clack, click, clack, click, clack, click, clack! Dad - dy's shoes.

MINE

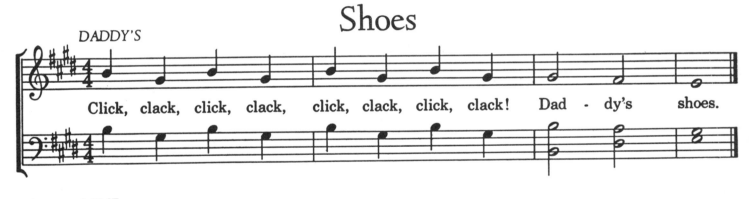

Tip-tap, tip-tap, tip-tap, tip-tap, tip-tap, tip-tap, tip-tap, tip-tap! Hear my shoes.

GRANDPA'S

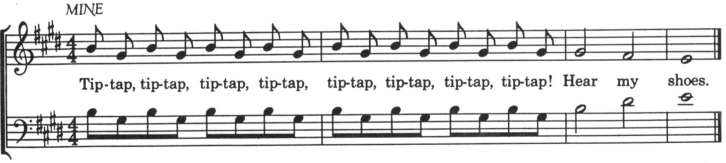

Shuf - fle, shuf - fle, Grand - pa's shoes.

About Our Toys

"And all my toys beside me lay
To keep me happy all the day."

R. L. S.

Jack-in-the-Box

Children's Song

Down in a box, still as still can be, Lift up the lid, What do you see? Pop up!

First child crouches down.   *Second child pretends to lift lid.*   *First child springs up, hands above head.*

Jumping Jack

Children's Song

Jump - ing jack, jump up and down, Up and down, up and down,

Up down, up down, Up down, stop!

I'm a Spinning Top

Children's Chant

I'm a spin-ning top, I'm a spin-ning top,

ritard

Round and round I go, Spin un - til I drop.

Listening: "The Top" (Impromptu), *Petite Suite,* Bizet. (Victor Listening Album One.)

127

Dolly

Patsy Parker

Doll - y, Doll - y, come and walk with me, Walk, walk, walk, walk, walk with me.

Teddy Bear

Alys E. Bentley

Doll - y's ly-ing in the clos - et Since my brown bear came;

He is shag-gy, big and wool - ly, Ted - dy is his name.

My Top

Grace Haynes

Paul Forde

Brightly

My top is sing-ing a hap-py song. Hum, hum, hum. It

sings to me a hap-py song. Hum, hum, hum.

128

Doll's Lullaby

Jewish

Sleep, ba - by doll,   Here on your bed,
Nu - mi bub - bah   Po ba mit - tah

Now night is here,   Sleep, my ba - by doll.
Hah - lei lah - bah,   Nu - mi bub - bah.

Dance, Dolly, Dance

Carl Reinecke

Allegretto

Tap triangle on beat.

Ting ting ting ting

p

Tap wood-block or rhythm stick on accented beat.

Tap tap tap tap

ten.

Imitative Play: Children will enjoy pretending to dance like dolls or parade like wooden soldiers.

We're Wooden Soldiers Marching

Mary Smith

Mary B. Black

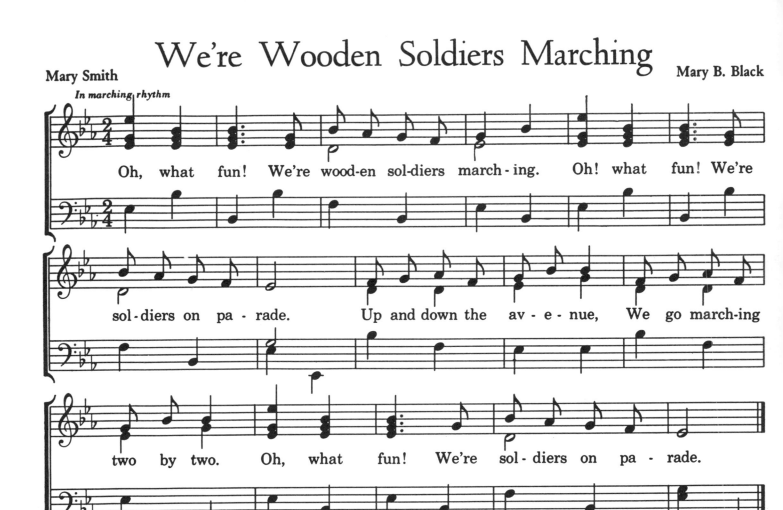

Oh, what fun! We're wood-en sol-diers march-ing. Oh! what fun! We're sol-diers on pa-rade. Up and down the av-e-nue, We go march-ing two by two. Oh, what fun! We're sol-diers on pa-rade.

Soldiers' March

Robert Schumann

Victor Rhythm Album Two.

130

About Trains and Planes and Other Things

Over the mountains,
Over the plains,
Over the rivers,
Here come the trains.

James S. Tippett

Playing Train: The songs and the piano selection ("Dance of the Moorish Slaves," Verdi) that follow are excellent for playing train. "Run, Run, Run," by Concone, p. 11, is also good for this activity.

Children imitate the rhythmic sounds of engines with very short and rapid sliding steps, their feet close to the floor. The feet are never lifted, but shuffled one after the other in quick succession.

A child is ready to be a part of a train after he has had his fill of being an engine, complete with whistle, bell, drivers, brakes, and steam.

Later a train of cars can be made by holding arms front at right angles, one child behind the other. The cars are "coupled" together when every child, except the engine, moves his hands forward and clasps the child in front of him by the wrists. The chain of arms act as wheel drivers, moving forward, down, and back, slowly at first, then faster and faster as the train picks up speed.

If the "engine" is careful, he can take his train over mountains, through tunnels, around the curves, across the plains and bridges, and safely back again into the station.

I Am a Big Train

131

Train

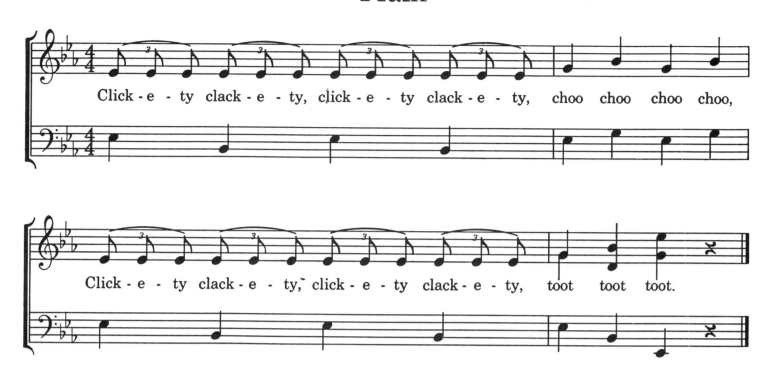

Click-e-ty clack-e-ty, click-e-ty clack-e-ty, choo choo choo choo,

Click-e-ty clack-e-ty, click-e-ty clack-e-ty, toot toot toot.

Playing Train • (Dance of the Moorish Slaves)

Giuseppe Verdi

I race him down the platform,
The puffing, snorting train.
He takes so long at starting
That it's not hard to gain
At first, but when his steam is up
He's haughty as can be;
He chuckles hoarsely to himself
Because he's passing me.

Rowena Bastin Bennett

All Aboard

All a-board, all a-board! Ding, ding, ding, ding.

Children sing C

Choo - choo - choo - choo, choo - ka, choo - ka, choo - ka, choo - ka,

Choo-ka choo-ka choo-ka choo-ka choo-ka choo-ka choo-ka choo-ka whoo whoooooooo ·

Children sing B natural.

who whooo Choo-ka choo-ka choo-ka choo-ka choo-ka choo-ka choo-ka choo-ka

Continue as train disappears in the distance.

133

Playing Airplane: For being airplanes see the piano selections suggested for being trains. (See page 131.)

Children use their feet to make the sound of the motor, just as they do for a train locomotive.

Freer and more flexible movements of the body are used to imitate the flight of a plane. Arms are stretched for wings while the body turns, dips, banks, and glides finally into port.

Airplane

I put my arms out so, And run and run and run.

Round and round I go, zzz *Children imitate sound of airplane as they run.*

I'm an Airplane

I'm an air-plane fly - ing, Hear my en - gine go - ing,

zzz *Children imitate sound of airplane as they run.*

In a Bus We Come

German

Rum tum tum, In a bus we come. Ride and ride and ride a - way,

134

In a Bus We Come (Continued)

In a bus we ride to-day. Rum tum tum, In a bus we come.

I'd Like to Be

Evelyn Cuthbert

E.C.

1. I'd like to be a big air-plane Up in the sky so blue. I'd
2. I'd like to be a big sail-boat Up-on the o-cean blue. I'd

fly a-round the great wide world, And then right back to you.
sail a-round the great wide world, And then right back to you.

Tugboat

Children's Song

Chug-chug, chug-chug, I'm a lit-tle tug-tug,
Chug-chug, chug-chug, I am push-ing big ships,

Chug-chug, chug-chug, Chug-ging night and day.
Chug-chug, chug-chug, All a-round the bay.

135

Watch the Lights!

M.M.

Marian Major

1. Watch the lights, watch the lights, Red says, "Stop!"
2. Watch the lights, watch the lights, Green says, "Go!"

Stop, Look and Listen

M.M.

Marian Major

Stop, look and lis - ten! Stop, look and lis - ten!

When you go to cross the tracks, Stop, look and lis - ten!

Who Will Ride the Bus?

M.M.

Marian Major

QUESTION   ANSWER

Who will ride the bus with me? I will, I will.

QUESTION   ANSWER

Who will drive the bus for me? I will, I will.

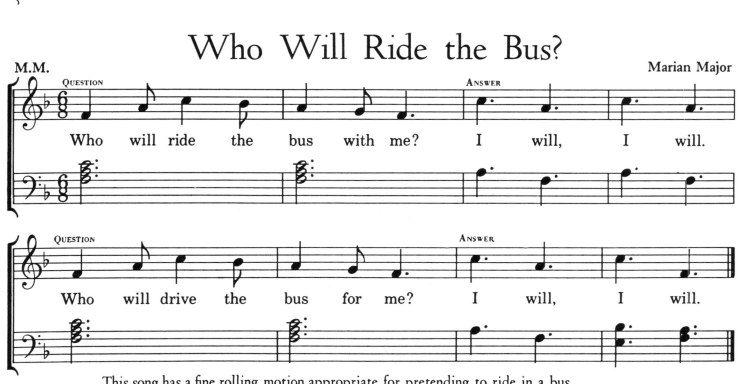

This song has a fine rolling motion appropriate for pretending to ride in a bus.
It may be used for individual response. See page 54, "The Knight of the Hobby Horse"

136

About Other Things That Sing

… let the woodwind flutes begin
Their elfin music, faint and thin.

Arthur Ketchum

About Playing Instruments: Keeping time to music is universally pleasure-giving. Percussion instruments are but extensions of patting feet, clapping hands, and snapping fingers. Assuming this to be true, drums, rhythm sticks, small cymbals, tambourines, and bells are examples of simple instruments that may be used advantageously for the enrichment of children's musical growth.

First of all, they can be useful in providing increasing direction, unity, and vitality to a child's innate desire to give objective expression to the compelling appeal of musical motion.

Percussion instruments are capable of being made a valuable means of developing tonal sensitivity in children. One drum may be higher or lower in pitch than another. Differences of tonal quality can be produced by striking a drum head in different places. There is considerable variation in both the quality and volume of drum tones. With proper guidance children can discover these things through their own experiments.

Implicit in learnings of this kind is careful listening And this can be carried over into more thoughtful attention to those songs and instrumental pieces which may be appropriately accompanied by percussion instruments.

To develop increasing discrimination children should be stimulated to become better listeners. And listening is pointed toward something that children can understand when their attention is directed toward choosing the instrument or instruments that will make the most fitting accompaniment for a given selection.

It will be noted that playing instruments has been suggested, whenever appropriate, throughout these pages. The material at this point is intended for the further enrichment of an already familiar expressive activity.

The songs that follow are typical of what any group of children can create when encouraged to sing what they play and to play what they sing.

The instrumental pieces are especially selected for young children. Each is simple enough for a little child to accompany with ease. While these selections are interesting musically, the variety of instruments for children to play can be very limited. Rhythm sticks, jingle clogs, and a triangle to accent rhythmic pulsation, with appropriate climactic drum beats or cymbal crashes, usually suffice.

In any case, it is advisable to avoid complexities of instrumentation and performance until the children themselves give indications of being ready to move on.

The Wood-Sticks

Tip-py, tap, tap and tick-y, tack, tick.

Do you hear the tap-ping of my wood-en stick?

137

Tip, Tip, Tap

Tip, tip, tap, the wood-stick's tap - ping, Tip, tip, tap, and tip - py, tap, tap.

The Triangle

Ring - a-ding-ding, hear the tri - an - gle sing. Ding-a-ding-ding, ding - a-ding-ding.

The Drum

Rat - a - tat - tat and rum - te - tum - tum, I will march and play the drum.

The Cymbals

Clang, cling, the cym - bals ring, Clang, cling, the cym - bals sing.

The Chimes of Dunkirk

Allegro *Bells, jingle sticks play rhythm of melody.*

Fine

Gong

Drums on accented beats throughout.

D.C. al Fine

138

Making Music

G.H.

Graham Haswell

1. Ting-a-ling-a-ling! Ting-a-ling-a-ling! Do you hear our bells?
2. Shake-a-shake-a-shake! Shake-a-shake-a-shake! Shake my tam-bou-rine.

Ting-a-ling-a-ling! Ting-a-ling-a-ling! Sweet-ly sing our bells.
Knock-a-knock-a-knock! Knock-a-knock-a-knock! On my tam-bou-rine.

Rataplan

Gaetano Donizetti

Allegro
Small drums

Big drum

Jingle, Jingle Johnny

Peter Thornton

German Folk Tune

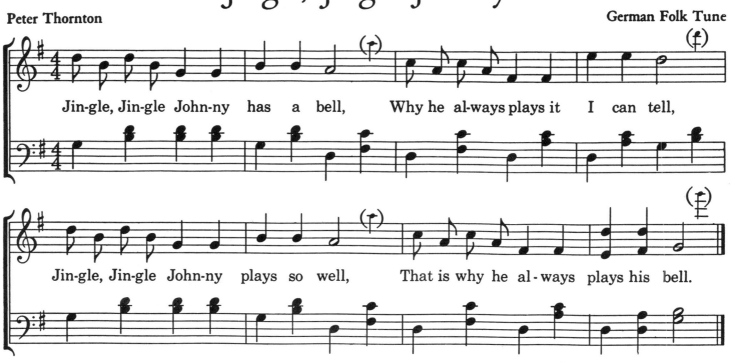

Jin-gle, Jin-gle John-ny has a bell, Why he al-ways plays it I can tell,

Jin-gle, Jin-gle John-ny plays so well, That is why he al-ways plays his bell.

Listening: "Evening Bells," Kullak. (Victor Listening Album Two.)

Le Tambourin

Jean Philippe Rameau

Jingle sticks play on notes that have grace notes before them.

140

Our Band Concert

By
Mildred Souers

Dramatization of songs and instrumental selections begins, of course, as an everyday classroom experience. Each is a way of giving more breadth and depth, as well as color and imagination, to music making. Each is therefore an important feature of a well-rounded music program.

Now and then small beginnings grow and spread beyond the classroom into the life of a school and from there into the community. This is what can happen with *Our Band Concert*. From simple beginnings it may develop into a program production suitable for public performance. Its success should suggest further developments. Here is a band ready to play several charming dance numbers. Why not create dances to be accompanied by the band?

Teachers and pupils will have their own ideas to add to those suggested here. For many, dramatic play of this type will remain play — a spontaneous classroom activity only. Others may need materials for public performance or special occasions.

A few or many varieties of instruments may be used. It will be noted that instruments of wood are more appropriate for the mood of one piece, while metal bells and clappers are more fitting for the spirit of other selections. All suggestions may be varied as desired.

Our Band Concert is arranged so that it may be performed without stopping between selections. However, each selection is complete and can be used independently.

Here Comes the Band

Here comes the band, oh so gay; Here comes the band, how they play. See them smile all the while, They're hap-py march-ing a - long. Here comes the band tall and straight, Al - ways on time, they're nev - er late.

On to their plac - es, see them go. Soon they'll be seat - ed row on row.

142

Dance of the Clowns

Dramatic Play: Listen to the music, imagining how a group of clowns would act. "If you were a clown, what would the music tell you to do?" Boys and girls will provide the answers.

Snowflake Dance

Dramatic Play: Children on tiptoe whirl about the stage in and around one another, with hands, arms, and fingers moving like whirling snowflakes.

*It is more effective if the bells are tapped or shaken lightly, only slightly accenting the first beat in each measure. However, where there are sustained tones, all bells should be jingled (shaken)

Spanish Dance

Tambourines, castanets, clave tone block*

knock, knock, shake

knock, knock,

clave tone block

shake

Dramatic Play: This dance may be performed by all girls — one group playing tambourines, the other, castanets. Or, boys may play the castanets.

*A clave tone block is appropriate for carrying the steady 1-2-3-4 beat of the
lower staff, while tambourines and castanets follow the melodic-rythmic pattern
of the upper staff.

Indian Hunting Dance

Barrel drums, tub drums, tom-toms. Also Indian rattles and whistles.

tom-toms

Dramatic Play: "What do Indian braves do when they are hunting deer?"

Scarf Dance

Dramatic Play for Scarf Dance: Added to or substituted for scarves could be large kerchiefs or wide ribbon streamers. The latter, made of crepe paper or paper muslin, are effective, and both come in a variety of colors.

The music for this dance is a light, graceful waltz suggesting free, improvisational movement. (See pp. xvi-xvii, *Rhythmic Expression*. E. Apparatus, Materials, etc.)

Prancing Ponies

*(Claves, clappers, coconut shells, wood blocks or "pat-a-cakes"
for marking time.)*

wood sticks and pat-a-cake blocks

claves and coconut shells

D.C. al Fine

Dramatic Play: Stick-horses with fanciful heads and bridles would make this
dance more colorful and exciting. A set pattern is unnecessary. "What does
the music tell you the ponies are doing?"

148

Spring Flower Bells

By
Catherine Frasetto Reilly

"Spring Flower Bells" may be performed effectively by either large or small groups of bunnies, fairies, and spring flowers, appropriately costumed. A bunny stands in each of the three circles, in the center of which there is a large flower bell suspended from a metal standard of the type used in gymnasiums. A long cord is fastened to the top of each bell. Other bunnies, fairies, and flowers carry small bells, which may be easily made by decorating jingle bells with crepe paper, cloth, or papier-mâché.

As an introduction, the following may be read by an older child or a teacher off stage:

"It's spring! All over the land tinkling bells may be heard as they herald the coming of spring. Bunnies with pink ears and powder-puff tails ring carrot bells. Tiny fairies with gossamer wings awaken the sleeping flowers with the sound of tinkling fairy bells. Bluebells, golden daffodils, white lilies, and purple hyacinths ring their tiny bells, which seem to say, 'It's spring, it's spring, it's spring!'"

This music may be played by older children or a teacher on piano, bells, or chimes while the three bunnies in the circles *pretend* to ring the *large flower bells*:

Ringing Bells

While "Spring, Beautiful Spring" is played, all the bunnies, fairies, and flowers run on tiptoe to their places as shown in the illustration on page 149:

Spring, Beautiful Spring

Paul Lincke

150

Bunnies remain standing, and fairies and flowers sit on the floor in their proper circles and lines. Fairies sit tall, and flowers sit in a crouched position with their heads down as if in slumber.

The bunnies hop and nod their heads in time to the music, following the leader up and down the "bunny line":

Allegro - Sonata No. 5

Franz Joseph Haydn

Now the bunnies run about, weaving in and out among the rows of sleeping flowers, as this music is played:

Scherzo

Felix Mendelssohn, Op. 16, No. 2

The bunnies sit on the floor in their lines.

The next music is for the fairies, who arise and dance in three circles. They run and point their toe in time to the music:

Gavotte

François Joseph Gossec

As this waltz is played, the fairies sway in time to the music:

Voices of Spring

Johann Strauss, Op. 410

Now the fairies return to their places and sit on the floor in circles.

153

The flowers awaken slowly and gracefully:

To a Wild Rose

Edward MacDowell, Op. 51

(Flowers slowly raise heads.)

(Move arms like petals opening.)

(Sway in kneeling position.)

(Slowly rise to standing position.)   ritard

154

a tempo

(Sway in a standing position.)

(Turn and stretch.)

(Stop and pose with hands stretched upward.)

(Bring arms down.)

(Curtsy - - - - - -)

The flowers have awakened from their slumber, and now they step (R or L) and point their toe (Pt.R or Pt.L) gracefully as they dance up and down the flower lines:

Amaryllis

Henri Ghys

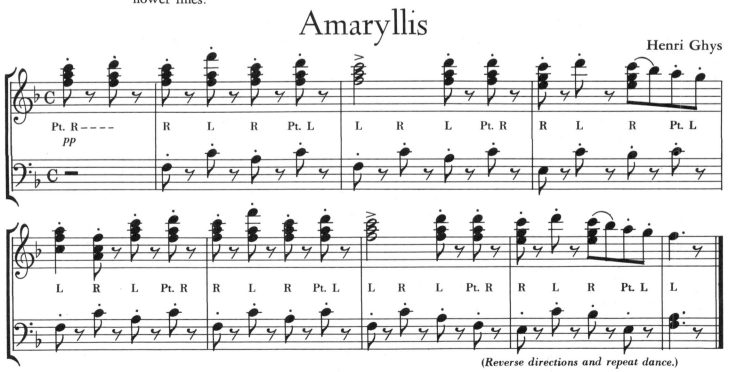

Pt. R - - - -   R   L   R   Pt. L   L   R   L   Pt. R   R   L   R   Pt. L

pp

L   R   L   Pt. R   R   L   R   Pt. L   L   R   L   Pt. R   R   L   R   Pt. L   L

(Reverse directions and repeat dance.)

The flowers remain standing.

155

Bunnies and fairies stand in their places. The three bunnies "ring" the *large flower bells* as the following melody is played on bells or chimes by a teacher or a group of older children:

Now the entire ensemble sways gracefully as they ring their *carrot bells,* *fairy bells,* and *flower bells:* (Allow the children to create their own interpretation of this waltz.)

Coppélia • Valse Lente

Léo Delibes

The dance has ended. The children curtsy and bow, then run off the stage on tiptoe. The entrance music, "Spring, Beautiful Spring," may be repeated as the children make their exit.

SHINING HOURS

To the land of Wonder-Wander,
Where the children love to go.

Eugene Field

Song meanings go deep, and tunes and tales go together. No fairy godmother could bestow richer gifts upon a child than a lively interest in song and story. For children grow in spirit upon those things which arouse in them gaiety and delight, wonder and beauty.

Realistic pictures of life are not enough for wholesome growth. Children need to have the realities of ordinary experience counterbalanced with the sense of timelessness which may be found in the world of imagination.

This section gives special emphasis to musical adventures that are associated with experiences in the "land of Wonder-Wander." There is no greater magic for evoking "shining hours" than that which is wrought by combining story and song. The song stories that follow are musical interpretations of folk tales beloved by countless boys and girls the world over. They tell of simple things in words and melodies and rhythms that children can speak and sing and act and understand.

So these song stories are already bright in the hearts of the young. This union with music makes them glow with a radiance that will light for children shining paths to new delights in timeless lands.

The two song-stories that follow in this book are recorded by Decca and are sung by Frank Luther.

| The Little Red Hen | No. C.U.S. 11 |
| Goldilocks and the Three Bears | No. C.U.S. 9 |

The Little Red Hen · Part One

By Frank Luther

This is the story of the little red hen.

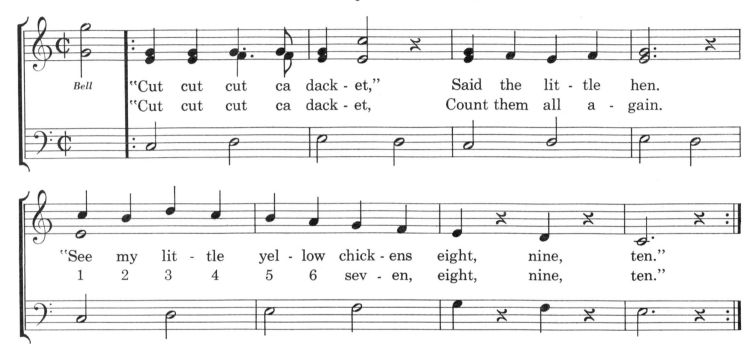

Bell

"Cut cut cut ca dack - et," Said the lit - tle hen.
"Cut cut cut ca dack - et, Count them all a - gain.

"See my lit - tle yel - low chick - ens eight, nine, ten."
1 2 3 4 5 6 sev - en, eight, nine, ten."

**One morning the little red hen found some little grains
of wheat in the little red barn. She said,**

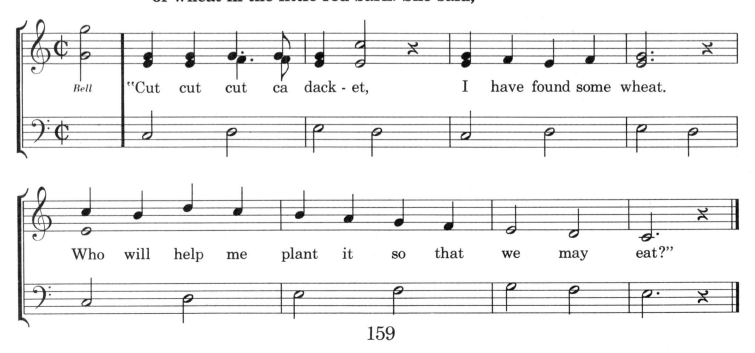

Bell

"Cut cut cut ca dack - et, I have found some wheat.

Who will help me plant it so that we may eat?"

159

The cat said, "I won't." The pig said, "I won't." The
frog said, "I won't, I won't, I won't, I won't."

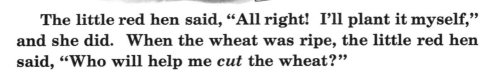

The little red hen said, "All right! I'll plant it myself,"
and she did. When the wheat was ripe, the little red hen
said, "Who will help me *cut* the wheat?"

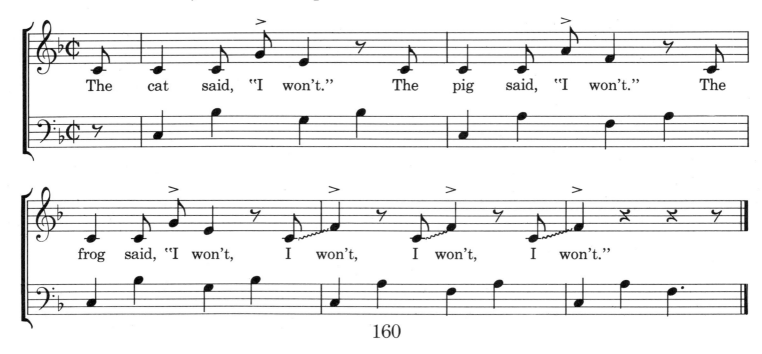

The cat said, "I won't." The pig said, "I won't." The
frog said, "I won't, I won't, I won't, I won't."

The little red hen said, "All right! I'll cut it myself,"
and she did.

The lit-tle red hen cut the wheat, cut cut, cut cut, cut cut, Oh, the

lit-tle red hen cut the wheat, cut cut, cut cut went the lit-tle red hen.

Then the little red hen said, "Who'll help me take the
wheat to the *mill*?"

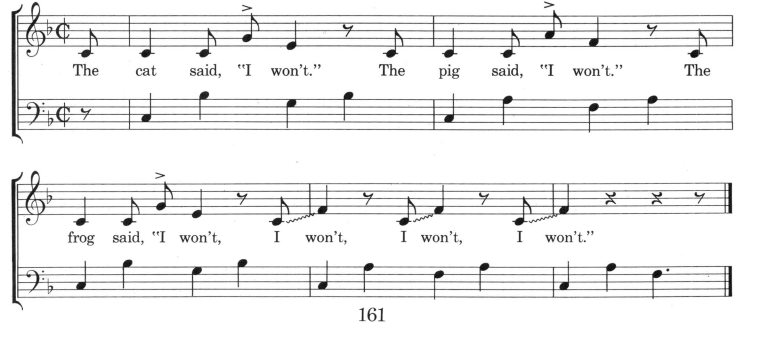

The cat said, "I won't." The pig said, "I won't." The

frog said, "I won't, I won't, I won't, I won't."

161

The little red hen said, "All right! I'll do it myself," and she did. She put the sack of wheat on her little red wheelbarrow and away she went to the mill, with the little red wheelbarrow wheel squeaking merrily.

squeak   *squeak*   A-way we go to the mill,   The mill just o-ver the hill.   The

squeak   *squeak*   *squeak*   *squeak*

mill-er will grind the wheat to flour,   He on-ly charg-es a pen-ny an hour.   A-

squeak   *squeak*   *squeak*   *squeak*

way we go to the mill,   ·   A - way we go to the mill.

squeak   *squeak*   *squeak*   *squeak*

When she got to the mill, the miller said, "Good morning, Little Red Hen, do you want your wheat made into nice whole wheat flour?" The little red hen said she did, so the miller started the mill wheel turning; and as the mill wheel went round, the little red hen sang, and the miller sang, too.

HEN
Cut cut cut ca dack - et, Cut cut cut ca dack - et,

MILLER
Grind - ing up the grain In the sun or rain,
Grind - ing up the wheat In the cold or heat,

MILL WHEEL

Cut cut cut ca dack - et, Cut cut cut ca dack - et.

All day long I sing my song and grind the grain.
All day long I sing my song and grind the wheat.

The miller put the flour in a little red sack. He put the little red *sack* in the little red *wheelbarrow* and the little red *hen* started home, with the little red *wheelbarrow wheel* squeaking merrily.

squeak   squeak

Home we come from the mill, · The mill just o - ver the hill. · I'll

squeak   squeak   squeak   squeak

take   my sack   of   whole wheat flour And   bake some bread in   half   an hour.

squeak   squeak   squeak   squeak

Home we come from the   mill,   Home we come from the   mill.

squeak   squeak   squeak   squeak

When she got home, the little red hen said, "Now who'll help me *bake* this flour into nice whole wheat bread?"

The cat said, "I won't." The pig said, "I won't." The frog said, "I won't, I won't, I won't, I won't."

The little red hen said, "All right! I'll bake it myself," and she did. When the bread came out of the oven, nice and brown and tasty, the little red hen said, "Now who'll help me *slice* the bread, and put butter and honey on the slices?"

The cat said, "I won't." The pig said, "I won't." The frog said, "I won't, I won't, I won't, I won't."

165

The little red hen said, "All right! I'll do it myself,"
and she did.

Bell

Slice, slice, the bread looks nice; Spread, spread, but-ter on the bread.

On top put hon-ey so sweet, Now it's time for us to eat.

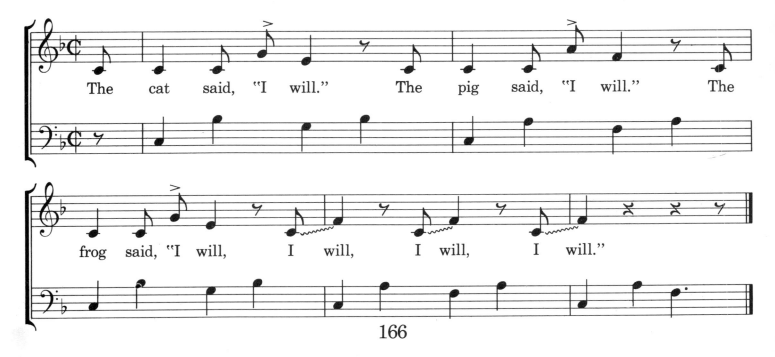

Then the little red hen said, "Now—who will help me
eat the bread all covered with butter and honey?"

The cat said, "I will." The pig said, "I will." The

frog said, "I will, I will, I will, I will."

The little red hen said, "You wouldn't help me with the work, so why should you eat?" The cat said, "That's right." The pig said, "That's right." The frog said, "That's right." And the little red hen called to her baby chickens, 8, 9, 10.

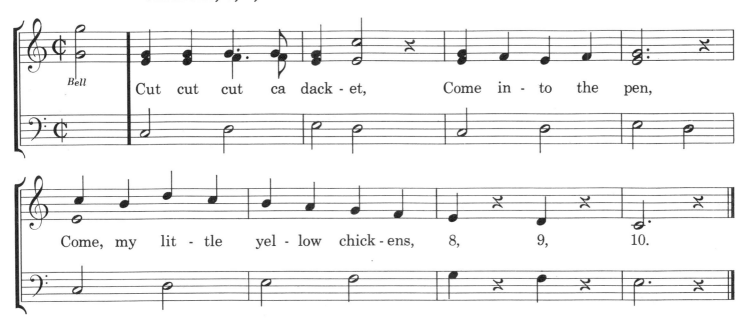

Bell

Cut cut cut ca dack - et,   Come in - to the pen,

Come, my lit - tle   yel - low chick - ens,   8,   9,   10.

And the little red hen and her chickens had a fine feast.

Goldilocks and the Three Bears · By Frank Luther

Part One

This is the story of Goldilocks and the Three Bears.

(✗ = note without tonal value)

168

In the living room canary birds were singing; and in
front of the fireplace

C

Great Big Bear had a great big chair, Mid-dle-siz'd bear had a mid-dle-siz'd chair,

Ba - by Bear had a lit-tle ba-by chair With a cush-ion of blue and pink.

In the dining room, on the table

D

Great Big Bear had a great big bowl, Mid-dle-siz'd bear had a mid-dle-siz'd bowl,

Ba - by Bear had a lit-tle ba-by bowl, With his name paint-ed on in pink.

169

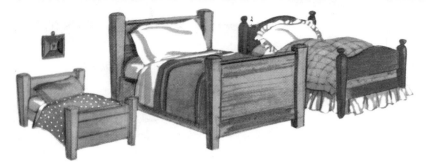

Do you know what was up in the bedroom?

E

Great Big Bear had a great big bed, Mid-dle-siz'd Bear had a mid-dle-siz'd bed,

Ba - by Bear had a lit-tle ba-by bed With a pil-low and quilt of pink.

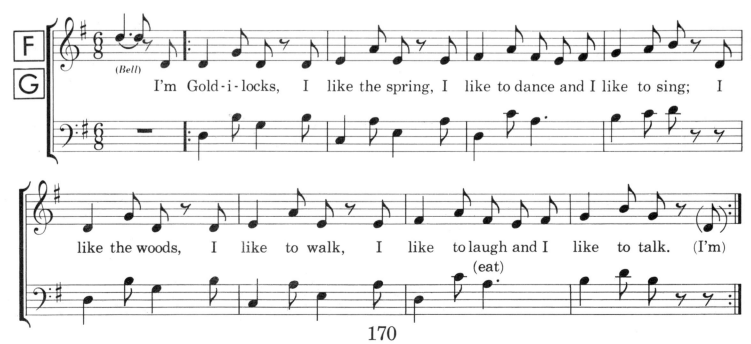

One day the three bears went for a walk, and while they were gone a little girl came skipping through the wood, singing this song.

F
G

(Bell)

I'm Gold-i-locks, I like the spring, I like to dance and I like to sing; I

like the woods, I like to walk, I like to laugh and I like to talk. (I'm)
(eat)

170

Goldilocks went skipping through the woods 'til she came to the little pink house. The door was open; so she walked right into the living room, where she saw the three chairs.

She tried the big chair but it was too hard, She tried the mid-dle chair but it was too soft; She tried the lit-tle chair and it was just right, But when she sat down it broke.

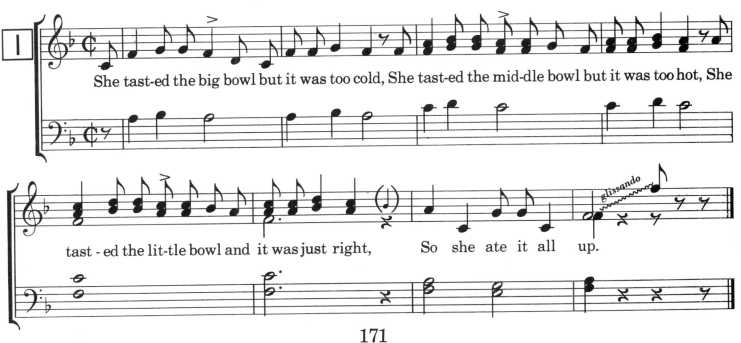

Goldilocks went into the dining room, where she saw the three bowls of porridge.

She tast-ed the big bowl but it was too cold, She tast-ed the mid-dle bowl but it was too hot, She tast-ed the lit-tle bowl and it was just right, So she ate it all up.

171

Then she went into the bedroom.

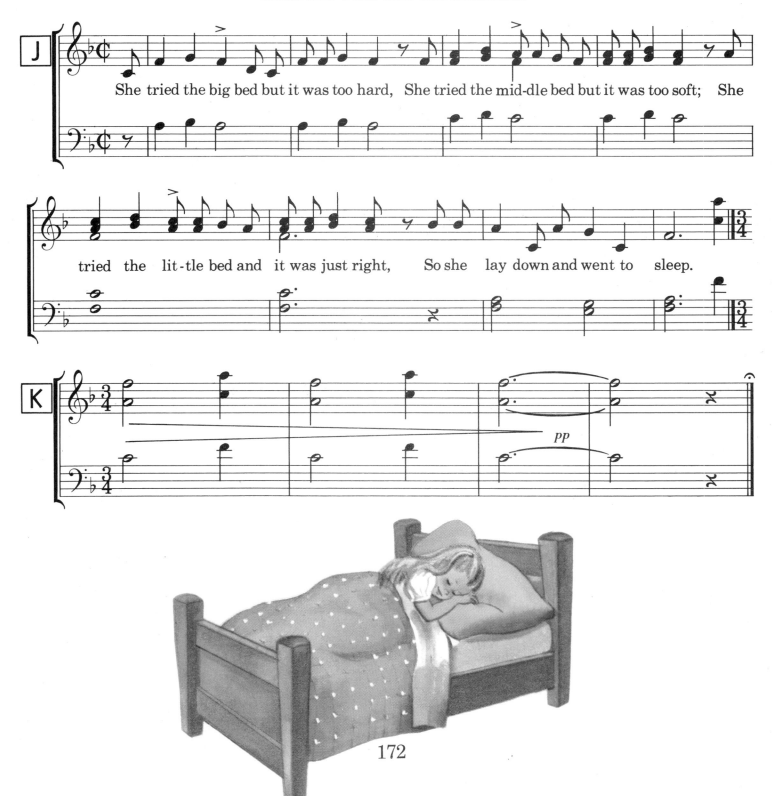

J She tried the big bed but it was too hard, She tried the mid-dle bed but it was too soft; She

tried the lit-tle bed and it was just right, So she lay down and went to sleep.

K

pp

Part Two

Like a march

L

(*Spoken*) Soon the bears came home and walked in-to their liv-ing room. Said

M

f

Great Big Bear, "Some-bod-y's been sit-ting in my chair."

mf

Said Mid-dle-siz'd Bear, "Some-bod-y's been sit-ting in

my chair."·

Said Ba-by Bear, "Some-bod-y's been sit-ting in

p (plaintively)

my chair · And broke it all up, And broke it all up."

Then they went in-to the din-ing room. Said

f

Great Big Bear, "Some-bod-y's been tast-ing my por - ridge."

Said Mid-dle-siz'd Bear, "Some-bod-y's been tast-ing my por-ridge."

Said Ba — by Bear, "Some-bod-y's been tast-ing my por — ridge

And ate it all up, And ate it all up."

Then · they went in-to the bed - room. Said

Great Big Bear, "Some-bod-y's been sleep-ing in my bed."

Said Mid-dle-siz'd Bear, "Some-bod-y's been sleep-ing in my bed."

Said Ba - by Bear, "Some-bod-y's been sleep-ing in my bed,

And look! There she is!"

Just then Goldilocks woke up!

Goldilocks jumped out of bed!

Goldilocks jumped out of the room!

Goldilocks jumped out of the little pink house!

177

And Goldilocks ran home as fast as she could run.

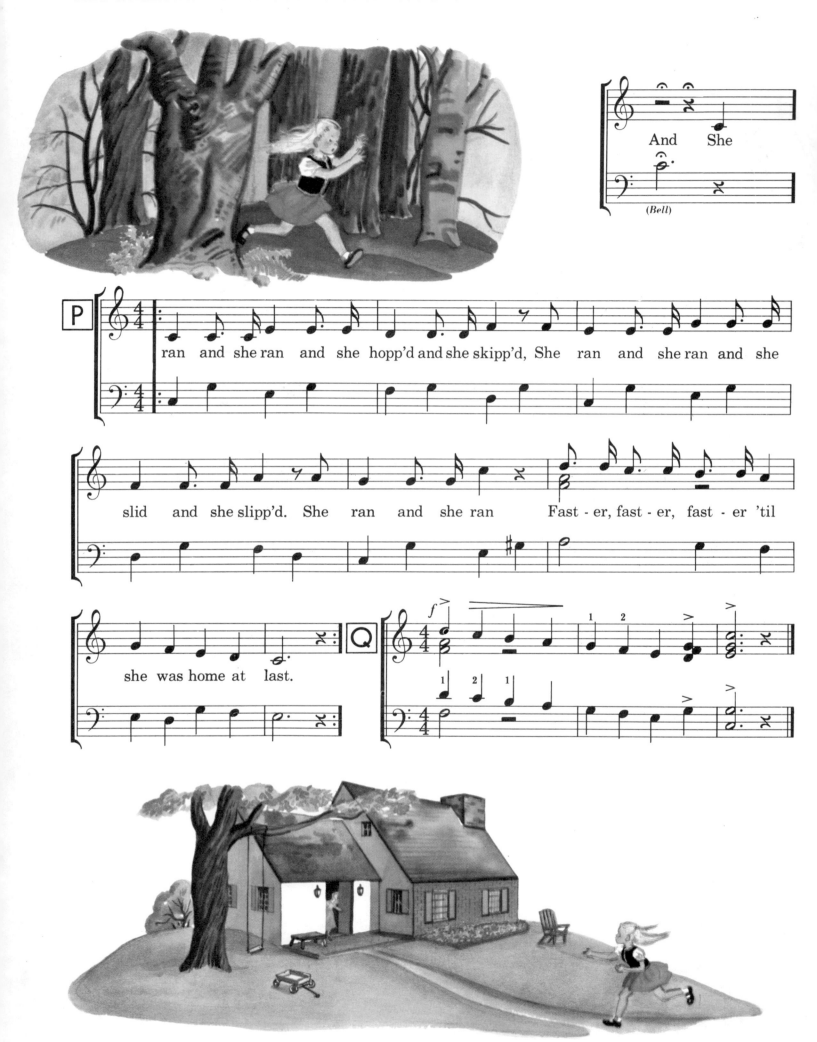

And   She

(Bell)

P ran and she ran and she hopp'd and she skipp'd, She ran and she ran and she

slid and she slipp'd. She ran and she ran Fast-er, fast-er, fast-er 'til

she was home at last. Q

ALPHABETICAL INDEX

Recorded songs are identified by the album numbers (K–A) and (K–B).
Titles in italics indicate instrumental selections.

179

INDEX OF FIRST LINES OF POEMS

PRINTED IN THE UNITED STATES OF AMERICA

Le Conte School,
Russell & Eilsworth Sts.
Berkeley 5, California